THE SPIRIT OF

PLACE

AN ANTHOLOGY MADE BY

RICHARD ALDINGTON

FROM THE PROSE OF

D · H · LAWRENCE

LONDON 1944

Readers Union

William Heinemann

The Places

This volume is produced in 1944 in complete conformity with the authorized economy standards. First published in 1935 by William Heinemann Ltd. it has been reset and printed by Butler & Tanner Ltd., Frome, Somerset. It is one of the books produced for sale to its members only by Readers Union Ltd., of 10–13 Bedford Street, London, and of Letchworth. Particulars of RU are obtainable from either of these addresses

EDITOR'S NOTE

THIS book is something less and something more than a prose Lawrence anthology. It is less, because the passages are nearly all taken from one part of his work—the novels and stories—and because they intentionally are limited to one aspect of his genius. But it is something more than an anthology which merely attempts to bring forward choice and characteristic specimens of an author's writing. There is a critical and indeed expository intention.

No doubt this intention could have been carried out by a critical exposition, but not many people read critical expositions, especially in that vaguely named " general public " for whom this book is hopefully intended. A critical exposition of Lawrence would be read chiefly by the already converted, who have doubtless long ago marked out these very passages in their collected editions. I address myself to the Lawrence opponents with a confident defiance, and with equally confident friendliness to those more numerous persons who for some reason find they " cannot get on with " this author. Certainly I might have expounded, but what is the need for that when the author speaks so admirably for himself? And I believe a demonstration is more convincing than any amount of abstract theorizing. There is seldom much point in writing about an author unless you admire him, and I think it more of a service to Lawrence's memory to show what is to be admired, than why. If you can find nothing to admire and to enjoy in the following pages, then I am sorry for you.

Not that this book contains *all* that I admire in Lawrence. As you read these passages, you will see that the title (which belongs to him) is no misnomer. It is always, or nearly always the Spirit of Place which is evoked—the experiences of that passionate sensibility which made Lawrence supreme in his time as the poet of the living world. Here is something of what he discovered and experienced in England and Italy, in Australia and America. The same world was open, is still open, to all other writers, yet from no other twentieth-century writer could such a collection as this be made. Here then is made, not a mere assertion, but a proof of something which Lawrence did in writing more perfectly and vividly than anyone else of his time. He felt this Spirit of Place more sensitively and beautifully than anyone else, and he set it down with a spontaneous mastery of English.

I do not give these passages as specimens of correct formal prose—you can find acres of that elsewhere—or as illustrations of any theory about how prose should be written. I do think the best of them represent that highest point in the art of writing where words achieve the miracle of becoming things, where we forget entirely to watch the writer's skill because we become wholly absorbed in the experience he is communicating. There is absolutely no labour to appear skilful, no self-consciousness. The " literary " taint, the " highbrow " appeal to snobbishness are entirely absent. There is no trace of freakishness or striving for originality, yet there is nothing commonplace. Nor are these mere purple passages. They occur perfectly naturally in the text, and the writing unconsciously rises with the theme. It is good to labour to be a great writer, but far better to be born one. Lawrence was born one.

Take three passages from this book—Lady Chatterley's drive through the industrial country of England, Monte Cassino and the peasant from the M.M. Memoirs, and the ranch scenes from St. Mawr. When I read those I am not conscious of " reading fine prose " ; I share an experience, and, what is more, an experience I could not have felt so intensely by myself. These experiences have become mine, Lawrence has given them to me. I feel that I too have driven with misgiving and despair past those raw mining towns and crumbling mansions under the great plumes of smoke and steam ; I too have stood in the bleak twilight by the cold monastery and have felt my heart break I knew not why ; and I too have stood at the door of the adobe cottage by the great pine-tree looking over the desert to the blue mountains, and feeling the strange non-human beauty ot it all. It is a great power in a writer if he can affect us so intensely and vitally—in comparison mere literary skill is a small thing.

But there is nothing to be gained by "discussing" and "analysing" such writing. That is all vanity and vexation of spirit. The only thing to do is to respond to it, to accept its enrichment, and to be grateful. And if you must "criticize," I will reveal to you the infallible method—go and do it better.

These passages of the Spirit of Place have also been chosen because I believe they illustrate a side of Lawrence which is most accessible to English writers, and most likely to delight them. This love of the non-human world both for its own sake and in its relations with human beings is not peculiar to English literature, but is a strong and persistent feature, as everyone recognizes. French literature always tends to become absorbed in purely human and social interests; with the Italians of the Renaissance "Nature" was a theme for very formal treatment, while with the modern Italians it is a theme for rhetorical treatment and is made to share the hysteria of the protagonists. In Spain, Azorin is a great exception—for him the visible world exists and he is almost perfect in his evocation of the unique moment of the Spirit of Place. But for him the spirit of time past is as important—Una Hora d'Espagna—and there is always the human figure, always the Latin tendency to conventional formal abstraction. The world of the English is wider and more irregular. They are picture-thinkers, but the picture moves. They are conscious of the other life which is not merely human, and for them it is really alive. Lawrence is here in the English tradition, but he does not fall into Ruskin's pathetic fallacy. He does not expect Nature to sympathize with his moods, though he may adapt his to Nature.

I think many English readers intensely enjoy experiences of this kind, and if they have not yet discovered that Lawrence can provide them almost more abundantly and vividly than any other writer, the reason is that they have not looked carefully enough. This Lawrence I have tried here to reveal, not of course to the many who already know him, but to that other many who have been "put off," either by what they may have heard or by unexpected and (to them) disagreeable aspects of the books.

It would have been possible greatly to extend these extracts, even from the novels and stories. There are four books of

Lawrence's which are almost entirely devoted to the Spirit of Place—*Twilight in Italy*, *Sea and Sardinia*, *Mornings in Mexico* and *Etruscan Places*. But if I had included them, I should have been indeed embarrassed how to choose. Any reader who is attracted by this collection will certainly find enjoyment in those four books. The *Letters* and the various essays would have furnished me with still more material, but I have limited myself to one letter—*Leaving Europe*—and to three or four extracts from the non-fiction prose, including the fine passage from *Apocalypse* which gives the final clue to the meaning of the book. There are no fancy titles to the extracts, not that I couldn't have found them or even that I was lazy, but because I think them impertinent. Admittedly this makes reference difficult and sometimes the theme of the quotation may not be wholly clear—in which case the reader can always refer to the context in the book quoted. I am anxious that this book should serve not as a substitute for reading Lawrence, but as an inducement to read him, and to read him with attention.

R. A.

E N G L A N D

From *THE WHITE PEACOCK*

WE crossed the tangle of fern and bracken, bramble and wild raspberry canes that spread in the open space before the house, and we went down the grassy slope to the edge of Nethermere. The wind whipped up noisy little wavelets, and the cluck and clatter of these among the pebbles, the swish of the rushes and the freshening of the breeze against our faces, roused us.

The tall meadow-sweet was in bud along the tiny beach and we walked knee-deep among it, watching the foamy race of the ripples and the whitening of the willows on the far shore. At the place where Nethermere narrows to the upper end, and receives the brook from Strelley, the wood sweeps down and stands with its feet washed round with waters. We broke our way along the shore, crushing the sharp-scented wild mint, whose odour checks the breath, and examining here and there among the marshy places ragged nests of water-fowl, now deserted. Some slim young lapwings started at our approach, and sped lightly from us, their necks outstretched in straining fear of that which could not hurt them. One, two, fled cheeping into cover of the wood ; almost instantly they coursed back again to where we stood, to dart off from us at an angle, in an ecstasy of bewilderment and terror.

* * *

Some wooden horses careered gaily round, and the swing-boats leaped into the mild blue sky. We sat upon the stile, my mother and I, and watched. There were booths, and cocoa-nut shies and roundabouts scattered in the small field. Groups of children moved quietly from attraction to attraction. A deeply tanned man came across the field swinging two dripping buckets of water. Women looked from the doors of their brilliant caravans, and lean dogs rose lazily and settled down again under the steps. The fair moved slowly, for all its noise. A stout lady, with a husky masculine voice, invited the excited children into her peep-show. A swarthy man stood with his thin legs astride on the platform of the roundabouts, and sloping backwards, his mouth distended with a row of fingers, he whistled astonishingly to the coarse row of the organ, and his whistling sounded clear, like the flight of a wild goose high over the chimney tops, as he was carried round and round. A little fat man with an ugly swelling on his chest stood screaming from a filthy booth to a crowd of urchins, bidding them challenge a big, stolid young man who stood with folded arms, his fists pushing out his biceps. On being asked if he would undertake any of these prospective challenges, this young man nodded, not having yet attained a talking stage :—yes, he would take two at a time, screamed the little fat man with the big excrescence on his chest, pointing at the cowering lads and girls. Farther off, Punch's quaint voice could be heard when the cocoa-nut man ceased grinding out screeches from his rattle. The cocoa-nut man was wroth, for these youngsters would not risk a penny shy, and the rattle yelled like a fiend. A little girl came along to look at us, daintily licking an ice-cream sandwich. We were uninteresting, however, so she passed on to stare at the caravans.

We had almost gathered courage to cross the wakes, when the cracked bell of the church sent its note falling over the babble.

" One—two—three "—had it really sounded three? Then it rang on a lower bell—" One—two—three." A passing bell for a man! I looked at my mother—she turned away from me.

The organ flared on—the husky woman came forward to make another appeal. Then there was a lull. The man with the lump on his chest had gone inside the rag to spar with the solid fellow. The cocoa-nut man had gone to the "Three Tunns" in fury, and a brazen girl of seventeen or so was in charge of the nuts. The horses careered round, carrying two frightened boys.

Suddenly the quick, throbbing note of the low bell struck again through the din. I listened—but could not keep count. One, two, three, four—for the third time that great lad had determined to go on the horses, and they had started while his foot was on the step, and he had been foiled—eight, nine ten—no wonder that whistling man had such a big Adam's apple—I wondered if it hurt his neck when he talked, being so pointed—nineteen, twenty—the girl was licking more ice-cream, with precious, tiny licks—twenty-five, twenty-six—I wondered if I did count to twenty-six mechanically. At this point I gave it up, and watched for Lord Tennyson's bald head to come spinning round on the painted rim of the roundabouts, followed by a red-faced Lord Roberts, and a villainous-looking Disraeli.

"Fifty-one——" said my mother. "Come—come along."

* * *

"Hold! Look out!" shouted the father excitedly, and immediately after a rabbit broke from the cover.

"Ay—Ay—Ay," was the shout, "turn him—turn him!" We set off full pelt. The bewildered little brute scared by Leslie's wild running and crying, turned from its course, and dodged across the hill, threading its terrified course through the maze of lying sheaves, spurting on in a painful zigzag, now bounding over an untied bundle of corn, now swerving from the sound of a shout. The little wretch was hard pressed; George rushed upon it. It darted into some fallen corn, but he had seen it, and had fallen on it. In an instant he was up again, and the little creature was dangling from his hand.

We returned, panting, sweating, our eyes flashing, to the edge of the standing corn. I heard Lettie calling, and turning round saw Emily and the two children entering the field as they passed from school.

"There's another!" shouted Leslie.

I saw the oat-tops quiver. "Here! Here!" I yelled. The animal leaped out, and made for the hedge. George and Leslie, who were on that side, dashed off, turned him, and he coursed back our way. I headed him off to the father who swept in pursuit for a short distance, but who was too heavy for the work. The little beast made towards the gate, but this time Mollie, with her hat in her hand and her hair flying, whirled upon him, and she and the little fragile lad sent him back again. The rabbit was getting tired. It dodged the sheaves badly, running towards the top hedge. I went after it. If I could have let myself fall on it I could have caught it, but this was impossible to me, and I merely prevented its dashing through the hole into safety. It raced along the hedge-bottom. George tore after it. As he was upon it, it darted into the hedge. He fell flat, and shot his hand into the gap. But it had escaped. He lay there, panting in great sobs, and looking at me with eyes in which excitement and exhaustion struggled like flickering light and darkness. When he could speak, he said, "Why didn't you fall on top of it?"

"I couldn't," said I.

* * *

After a while we went out also, before the light faded altogether from the pond. Emily took us into the lower garden to get some ripe plums. The old garden was very low. The soil was black. The cornbind and goosegrass were clutching at the ancient gooseberry bushes, which sprawled by the paths. The garden was not very productive, save of weeds, and, perhaps, tremendous lank artichokes or swollen marrows. But at the bottom, where the end of the farm buildings rose high and grey, there was a plum-tree which had been crucified to the wall, and which had broken away and leaned forward from bondage. Now under the boughs were hidden great mist-bloomed, crimson treasures, splendid globes. I shook the old, ragged trunk, green, with even the fresh gum dulled over, and the treasures fell heavily, thudding down among the immense rhubarb leaves below. The girls laughed, and we divided the spoil, and turned back to the yard. We went down to the edge of the garden, which skirted the bottom pond, a pool chained in a heavy growth of weeds. It was moving with rats, the father had said. The rushes were thick below us ; opposite, the great bank fronted us, with orchard trees climbing it like a hillside. The lower pond received the overflow from the upper by a tunnel from the deep black sluice.

Two rats ran into the back culvert at our approach. We sat on some piled, mossy stones, to watch. The rats came out again, ran a little way, stopped, ran again, listened, were reassured, and slid about freely, dragging their long naked tails. Soon six or seven grey beasts were playing round the mouth of the culvert, in the gloom. They sat and wiped their sharp faces, stroking their whiskers. Then one would give a little rush and a little squirm of excitement and would jump vertically into the air, alighting on four feet, running, sliding into the black shadow. One dropped with an ugly plop into the water, and swam towards us, the hoary imp, his sharp snout, and his wicked little eyes moving at us. Lettie shuddered. I threw a stone into the dead pool, and frightened them all. But we had frightened ourselves more, so we hurried away, and stamped our feet in relief on the free pavement of the yard.

* * *

I was born in September, and love it best of all the months. There is no heat, no hurry, no thirst and weariness in corn harvest as there is in the hay. If the season is late, as is usual with us, then mid-September sees the corn still standing in stook. The mornings come slowly. The earth is like a woman married and fading ; she does not leap up with a laugh for the first fresh kiss of dawn, but slowly, quietly, unexpectantly lies watching the waking of each new day. The blue mist, like memory in the eyes of a neglected wife, never goes from the wooded hill, and only at noon creeps from the near hedges. There is no bird to put a song in the throat of morning ; only the crow's voice speaks during the day. Perhaps there is the regular breathing hush of the scythe—even the fretful jar of the mowing machine. But next day, in the morning, all is still again. The lying corn is wet, and when you have bound it, and lift the heavy sheaf to make the stook, the tresses of oats wreathe round each other and droop mournfully.

* * *

We tramped down to dinner with only the clinging warmth of the sunshine for a coat. In this still, enfolding weather a quiet companionship is very grateful. Autumn creeps through everything. The little damsons in the pudding taste of September and are fragrant with memory. The voices of those at table are softer and more reminiscent than at haytime.

Afternoon is all warm and golden. Oat sheaves are lighter; they whisper to each other as they freely embrace. The long, stout stubble tinkles as the foot brushes over it; the scent of the straw is sweet. When the poor, bleached sheaves are lifted out of the hedge, a spray of nodding wild raspberries is disclosed, with belated berries ready to drop; among the damp grass lush blackberries may be discovered. Then one notices that the last bell hangs from the ragged spire of fox-glove. The talk is of people, an odd book; of one's hopes—and the future; of Canada, where work is strenuous, but not life; where the plains are wide, and one is not lapped in a soft valley, like an apple that falls in a secluded orchard. The mist steals over the face of the warm afternoon. The tying-up is all finished, and it only remains to rear up the fallen bundles into shocks. The sun sinks into a golden glow in the west. The gold turns to red, the red darkens, like a fire burning low, the sun disappears behind the bank of milky mist, purple like the pale bloom on blue plums, and we put on our coats and go home.

* * *

At last, however, winter began to gather her limbs, to rise, and drift with saddened garments northward.

The strike was over. The men had compromised. It was a gentle way of telling them they were beaten. But the strike was over.

The birds fluttered and dashed; the catkins on the hazel loosened their winter rigidity, and swung soft tassels. All through the day sounded long, sweet whistlings from the brushes; then later, loud, laughing shouts of bird triumph on every hand.

I remember a day when the breast of the hills was heaving in a last quick waking sigh, and the blue eyes of the waters opened bright. Across the infinite skies of March great rounded masses of cloud had sailed stately all day, domed with a white radiance, softened with faint, fleeting shadows as if companies of angels were gently sweeping past; adorned with resting, silken shadows like those of a full white breast. All day the clouds had moved on to their vast destination, and I had clung to the earth yearning and impatient. I took a brush and tried to paint them, then I raged at myself. I wished that in all the wild valley where cloud shadows were travelling like pilgrims, something would call me forth from my rooted loneliness. Through all the grandeur of the white and blue day, the poised cloud masses swung their slow flight, and left me unnoticed. At evening, they were all gone, and the empty sky, like a blue bubble over us, swam on its pale bright rims.

* * *

So we went along by the hurrying brook, which fell over little cascades in its haste, never looking once at the primroses that were glimmering all along its banks. We turned aside and climbed the hill through the woods. Velvety green sprigs of dog-mercury were scattered on the red soil. We came to the top of a slope, where the wood thinned. As I talked to Emily I became dimly aware of a whiteness over the ground. She exclaimed with surprise, and I found that I was walking, in the first shades of twilight, over clumps of snowdrops. The hazels were thin, and only here and there an oak tree uprose. All the ground was white with snowdrops, like drops of manna scattered over the red earth, on the grey-green clusters of leaves. There was a deep little dell, sharp sloping like a cup, and white sprinkling of flowers all the way down, with white flowers showing pale among the first inpouring of shadow at the bottom. The earth was red and warm, pricked with the dark, succulent green of bluebell sheaths, and embroidered with grey-green clusters of spears, and many white flowerets. High above, above the light tracery of hazel, the weird oaks tangled in the sunset. Below, in the first shadows, drooped hosts of little white flowers, so silent and sad; it seemed like a holy communion of pure wild things, numberless, frail, and folded meekly in the evening light. Other flower companies are glad; stately barbaric hordes of bluebells, merry-headed cowslip groups, even light, tossing wood-anemones; but snowdrops are sad and mysterious. We have lost their meaning. They do not belong to us, who ravish them. The girls bent among them, touching them with their fingers, and symbolizing the yearning which I felt. Folded in the twilight, these conquered flowerets are sad, like forlorn little friends of dryads.

* * *

The grassy path to the churchyard was still clogged with decayed leaves. The church is abandoned. As I drew near an owl floated softly out of the black tower. Grass overgrew the threshold. I pushed open the door, grinding back a heap of fallen plaster and rubbish, and entered the place. In the twilight the pews were leaning in ghostly disorder, the prayer-books dragged from their ledges, scattered on the floor in the dust and rubble, torn by mice and birds. Birds scuffled in the darkness of the roof. I looked up. In the upward well of the tower I could see a bell hanging. I stooped and picked up a piece of plaster from the ragged confusion of feathers, and broken nests, and remnants of dead birds. Up into the vault overhead I tossed pieces of plaster until one hit the bell, and it "tonged" out its faint remonstrance. There was a rustle of many birds, like spirits. I sounded the bell again, and dark forms moved with cries of alarm overhead, and something fell heavily. I shivered in the dark, evil-smelling place, and hurried to get out of doors. I clutched my hands with relief and pleasure when I saw the sky above me quivering with the last crystal lights, and the lowest red of sunset behind the yew-boles. I drank the fresh air, that sparkled with the sound of the blackbirds and thrushes whistling their strong bright notes.

I strayed round to where the headstones, from their eminence, leaned to look on the Hall below, where great windows shone yellow light on to the flagged courtyard, and the little fish pool. A stone staircase descended from the graveyard to the court, between stone balustrades whose pock-marked grey columns still swelled gracefully and with dignity, encrusted with lichens. The staircase was filled with ivy and rambling roses—impassable. Ferns were unrolling round the big square halting place, half-way down where the stairs turned.

A peacock, startled from the back premises of the Hall, came flapping up the terraces to the churchyard. Then a heavy footstep crossed the flags. It was the keeper. I whistled the whistle he knew, and he broke his way through the vicious rose-boughs up the stairs. The peacock flapped beyond me, on to the neck of an old bowed angel, rough and dark, an angel which had long ceased sorrowing for the lost Lucy, and had died also. The bird bent its voluptuous neck and peered about. Then it lifted up its head and yelled. The sound tore the dark sanctuary of twilight. The old grey grass seemed to stir, and I could fancy the smothered primroses and violets beneath it waking and gasping for fear.

* * *

They decided to bury him in our churchyard at Greymede under the beeches; the widow would have it so, and nothing might be denied her in her state.

It was a magnificent morning in early spring when I watched among the trees to see the procession come down the hillside. The upper air was woven with the music of the larks, and my whole world thrilled with the conception of summer. The young pale windflowers had arisen by the wood-gale, and under the hazels, when perchance the hot sun pushed his way, new little suns dawned, and blazed with real light. There was a certain thrill and quickening everywhere, as a woman must feel when she has conceived. A sallow tree in a favoured spot looked like a pale gold cloud of summer dawn; nearer it had poised a golden, fairy busby on every twig, and was voiced with a hum of bees, like any sacred golden bush, uttering its gladness in the thrilling murmur of bees, and in warm scent. Birds called and flashed on every hand; they made off exultant with streaming strands of grass, or wisps of fleece, plunging into the dark spaces of the wood, and out again into the blue.

A lad moved across the field from the farm below with a dog trotting behind him,—a dog, no, a fussy, black-legged lamb trotting along on its toes, with its tail swinging behind. They were going to the mothers on the common, who moved like little grey clouds among the dark gorse.

I cannot help forgetting, and sharing the spink's triumph, when he flashes past with a fleece from a bramble bush. It will cover the bedded moss, it will weave among the soft red cow-hair beautifully. It is a prize, it is an ecstasy to have captured it at the right moment, and the nest is nearly ready.

Ah, but the thrush is scornful, ringing out his voice from the hedge! He sets his breast against the mud, and models it warm for the turquoise eggs—blue, blue, bluest of eggs, which cluster so close and round against the breast, which round up beneath the breast, nestling content. You should see the bright ecstasy in the eyes of a nesting thrush, because of the rounded caress of the eggs against her breast!

What a hurry the jenny wren makes—hoping I shall not see her dart into the low bush. I have a delight in watching them against their shy little wills. But they have all risen with a rush of wings, and are gone, the birds. The air is brushed with agitation. There is no lark in the sky, not one; the heaven is clear of wings or twinkling dot——.

Till the heralds come—till the heralds wave like shadows in the bright air, crying, lamenting, fretting for ever. Rising and falling and circling round and round, the slow-waving peewits cry and complain, and lift their broad wings in sorrow. They stoop suddenly to the ground, the lapwings, then in another throb of anguish and protest, they swing up again, offering a glistening white breast to the sunlight, to deny it in black shadow, then a glisten of green, and all the time crying and crying in despair.

The pheasants are frightened into cover, they run and dart through the hedge. The cold cock must fly in his haste, spread himself on his streaming plumes, and sail into the wood's security.

There is a cry in answer to the peewits, echoing louder and

stronger the lamentation of the lapwings, a wail which hushes the birds. The men come over the brow of the hill, slowly, with the old squire walking tall and straight in front; six bowed men bearing the coffin on their shoulders, treading heavily and cautiously, under the great weight of the glistening white coffin; six men following behind, ill at ease, waiting their turn for the burden. You can see the red handkerchiefs knotted round their throats, and their shirt-fronts blue and white between the open waistcoats. The coffin is of new unpolished wood, gleaming and glistening in the sunlight; the men who carry it remember all their lives after the smell of new, warm elm-wood.

Again a loud cry from the hill-top. The woman has followed thus far, the big, shapeless woman, and she cries with loud cries after the white coffin as it descends the hill, and the children that cling to her skirts weep aloud, and are not to be hushed by the other woman, who bends over them, but does not form one of the group. How the crying frightens the birds, and the rabbits; and the lambs away there run to their mothers. But the peewits are not frightened, they add their notes to the sorrow; they circle after the white, retreating coffin, they circle round the woman; it is they who for ever "keen" the sorrows of this world. They are like priests in their robes, more black than white, more grief than hope, driving endlessly round and round, turning, lifting, falling and crying always in a mournful desolation, repeating their last syllables like the broken accents of despair.

The bearers have at last sunk between the high banks, and turned out of sight. The big woman cannot see them, and yet she stands to look. She must go home, there is nothing left.

They have rested the coffin on the gate posts, and the bearers are wiping the sweat from their faces. They put their hands to their shoulders on the place where the weight has pressed. The other six are placing the pads on their shoulders, when a girl comes up with a jug, and a blue pot. The squire drinks first, and fills for the rest. Meanwhile the girl stands back under the hedge, away from the coffin which smells of new elm-wood. In imagination she pictures the man shut up there in close darkness, while the sunlight flows all outside, and she catches her breast with terror. She must turn and rustle among the leaves of the violets for the flowers she does not see. Then, trembling, she comes to herself, and plucks a few flowers and breathes them hungrily into her soul, for comfort. The men put down the pots beside her, with thanks, and the squire gives the word. The bearers lift up the burden again, and the elm-boughs rattle along the hollow white wood, and the pitiful red clusters of elm-flowers sweep along it as if they whispered in sympathy—" We are so sorry, so sorry——; " always the compassionate buds in their fullness of life bend down to comfort the dark man shut up there. " Perhaps," the girl thinks, " he hears them, and goes softly to sleep." She shakes the tears out of her eyes on to the ground, and, taking up her pots, goes slowly down, over the brooks.

* * *

When I went to bed I looked across at the lighted windows of Highclose, and the lights trailed mistily towards me across the water. The cedar stood dark guard against the house; bright the windows were, like the stars, and, like the stars, covering their torment in brightness. The sky was glittering with sharp lights—they are too far off to take trouble for us, so little, little almost to nothingness. All the great hollow vastness roars overhead, and the stars are only sparks that whirl and spin in the restless space. The earth must listen to us; she covers her face with a thin veil of mist, and is sad; she soaks up our blood tenderly, in the darkness, grieving, and in the light she soothes and reassures us. Here on our earth is sympathy and hope, the heavens have nothing but distances.

A corn-crake talked to me across the valley, talked and talked endlessly, asking and answering in hoarse tones from the sleeping, mist-hidden meadows. The monotonous voice that on past summer evenings had had pleasant notes of romance, now was intolerable to me. Its inflexible harshness and cacophony seemed like the voice of fate speaking out its tuneless perseverance in the night.

* * *

The wood was high and warm. Along the ridings the forget-me-nots were knee-deep, stretching glimmering into the distance like the Milky Way through the night. They left the tall, flower-tangled paths to go in among the bluebells, breaking through the close-pressed flowers and ferns till they came to an oak which had fallen across the hazels, where they sat half-screened. The hyacinths drooped magnificently with an over-weight of purple, or they stood pale and erect like unripe ears of purple corn. Heavy bees swung down in a blunder of extravagance among the purple flowers. They were intoxicated even with the sight of so much blue. The sound of their hearty, wanton humming came clear upon the solemn boom of the wind overhead. The sight of their clinging, clambering riot gave satisfaction to the soul. A rosy campion flower caught the sun and shone out. An elm sent down a shower of flesh-tinted sheaths upon them.

* * *

The magnificent promise of spring was broken before the May-blossom was fully out. All through the beloved month the wind rushed in upon us from the north and north-east, bringing the rain fierce and heavy. The tender-budded trees shuddered and moaned; when the wind was dry, the young leaves flapped limp. The grass and corn grew lush, but the light of the dandelions was quite extinguished, and it seemed that only a long time back had we made merry before the broad glare of these flowers. The bluebells lingered and lingered; they fringed the fields for weeks like purple fringe of mourning. The pink campions came out only to hang heavy with rain; hawthorn buds remained tight and hard as pearls, shrinking into the brilliant green foliage; the forget-me-nots, the poor pleiades of the wood, were ragged weeds. Often at the end of the day, the sky opened, and stately clouds hung over the horizon infinitely far away, glowing, through the yellow distance, with an amber lustre. They never came any nearer, always they remained far off, looking calmly and majestically over the shivering earth, then saddened, fearing their radiance might be dimmed, they drew away, and sank out of sight. Sometimes, towards sunset, a great shield stretched dark from the west to the zenith, tangling the light along its edges. As the canopy rose higher, it broke, dispersed, and the sky was primrose coloured, high and pale above the crystal moon. Then the cattle crouched among the gorse, distressed by the cold, while the long-billed snipe flickered round high overhead, round and round in great circles, seeming to carry a serpent from its throat, and crying a tragedy, more painful than the poignant lamentations and protests of the peewits. Following these evenings came mornings cold and grey.

* * *

I kicked through the drenched grass, crushing the withered cowslips under my clogs, avoiding the purple orchids that were stunted with harsh upbringing, but magnificent in their powerful colouring, crushing the pallid lady-smocks, the washed-out wild gillivers. I became conscious of something near my feet, something little and dark, moving indefinitely. I had found again the larkie's nest. I perceived the yellow beaks, the bulging eyelids of two tiny larks and the blue lines of their wing quills. The indefinite movement was the swift rise and fall of the brown fledged backs, over which waved long strands of fine down. The two little specks of birds lay side by side, beak to beak, their tiny bodies rising and falling in quick unison. I gently put down my fingers to touch them; they were warm; gratifying to find them warm, in the midst of so much cold and wet. I became curiously absorbed in them, as an eddy of wind stirred the strands of down. When one fledgling moved uneasily, shifting his soft ball, I was quite excited; but he nestled down again, with his head close to his brother's. In my heart of hearts, I longed for someone to nestle against, someone who would come between me and the coldness and wetness of the surroundings. I envied the two little miracles exposed to any tread, yet so serene. It seemed as if I were always wandering, looking for something which they had found even before the light broke into their shell. I was cold; the lilacs in the Mill garden looked blue and perished. I ran with my heavy clogs and my heart heavy with vague longing, down to the Mill, while the wind blanched the sycamores, and pushed the sullen pines rudely, for the pines were sulking because their million creamy sprites could not fly wet-winged. The horse-chestnuts bravely kept their white candles erect in the socket of every bough, though no sun came to light them. Drearily a cold swan swept up the water, trailing its black feet, clacking its great hollow wings, rocking the frightened water-hens, and insulting the staid black-necked geese. What did I want that I turned thus from one thing to another?

* * *

In a few moments we were on the top of the car swinging down to the Trent Bridges. It was dinner time, and crowds of people from shops and warehouses were hurrying in the sunshine along the pavements. Sunblinds cast their shadows on the shop-fronts, and in the shade streamed the people dressed brightly for summer. As our car stood in the great space of the market place we could smell the mingled scent of fruit, oranges, and small apricots, and pears piled in their vividly coloured sections on the stalls. Then away we sailed through the shadows of the dark streets, and the open pools of sunshine. The castle on its high rock stood in the dazzling dry sunlight; the fountain stood shadowy in the green glimmer of the lime-trees that surrounded the alms-houses.

* * *

I suffered acutely the sickness of exile in Norwood. For weeks I wandered the streets of the suburb, haunted by the spirit of some part of Nethermere. As I went along the quiet roads where the lamps in yellow loneliness stood among the leafless trees of the night I would feel the feeling of the dark, wet bit of path between the wood-meadow and the brooks. The spirit of that wild little slope to the Mill would come upon me, and there in the suburb of London I would walk wrapt in the sense of a small wet place in the valley of Nethermere. A strange voice within me rose and called for the hill path; again I could feel the wood waiting for me, calling and calling, and I crying for the wood, yet the space of many miles was between us.

Since I left the valley of home I have not much feared any other loss. The hills of Nethermere had been my walls, and the sky of Nethermere my roof overhead. It seemed almost as if, at home, I might lift my hand to the ceiling of the valley, and touch my own beloved sky, whose familiar clouds came again and again to visit me, whose stars were constant to me, born when I was born, whose sun had been all my father to me. But now the skies were strange over my head, and Orion walked past me unnoticing, he who night after night had stood over the woods to spend with me a wonderful hour. When does day now lift up the confines of my dwelling place, when does the night throw open her vastness for me, and send me the stars for company? There is no night in a city. How can I lose myself in the magnificent forest of darkness when night is only a thin scattering of the trees of shadow with barrenness of lights between!

I could never lift my eyes save to the Crystal Palace, crouching, cowering wretchedly among the yellow-grey clouds, pricking up its two round towers like pillars of anxious misery. No landmark could have been more foreign to me, more depressing, than the great dilapidated palace which lay forever prostrate above us, fretting because of its own degradation and ruin.

I watched the buds coming on the brown almond trees; I heard the blackbirds, and I saw the restless starlings; in the streets were many heaps of violets, and men held forward to me snowdrops whose white mute lips were pushed upwards in a bunch: but these things had no meaning for me, and little interest.

* * *

The spring came bravely, even in south London, and the town was filled with magic. I never knew the sumptuous purple of evening till I saw the round arc-lamps fill with light, and roll like golden bubbles along the purple dusk of the high road. Everywhere at night the city is filled with the magic of lamps: over the river they pour in golden patches their floating luminous oil on the restless darkness; the bright lamps float in and out of the cavern of London Bridge Station like round shining bees in and out of a black hive; in the suburbs the street lamps glimmer with the brightness of lemons among the trees. I began to love the town.

In the mornings I loved to move in the aimless street's procession, watching the faces come near to me, with the sudden glance of dark eyes, watching the mouths of the women blossom with talk as they passed, watching the subtle movements of the shoulders of men beneath their coats, and the naked warmth of their necks that went glowing along the street. I loved the city intensely for its movement of men and women, the soft, fascinating flow of the limbs of men and women, and the sudden flash of eyes and lips as they pass. Among all the faces of the street my attention roved like a bee which clambers drunkenly among blue flowers. I became intoxicated with the strange nectar which I sipped out of the eyes of the passers-by.

I did not know how time was hastening by on still bright wings, till I saw the scarlet hawthorn flaunting over the road, and the lime-buds lit up like wine drops in the sun and the pink scarves of the lime-buds pretty as louse-wort a-blossom in the gutters, and a silver-pink tangle of almond boughs against the blue sky. The lilacs came out, and in the pensive stillness of the suburb, at night, came the delicious tarry scent of lilac flowers, wakening the silent laughter of romance.

* * *

I wandered around Nethermere, which had now forgotten me. The daffodils under the boat-house continued their golden laughter, and nodded to one another in gossip, as I watched them, never for a moment pausing to notice me. The yellow reflection of daffodils among the shadows of grey willow in the water trembled faintly as they told haunted tales in the gloom. I felt like a child left out of the group of my playmates. There was a wind running across Nethermere, and on the eager water blue and glistening grey shadows changed places swiftly. Along the shore the wild birds rose, flapping in expostulation as I passed, peewits mewing fiercely round my head, while two white swans lifted their glistening feathers till they looked like grand double water-lilies, laying back their orange beaks among the petals, and fronting me with haughty resentment, charging towards me insolently.

I wanted to be recognized by something. I said to myself that the dryads were looking out for me from the wood's edge. But as I advanced they shrank, and glancing wistfully, turned back like pale flowers falling in the shadow of the forest. I was a stranger, an intruder. Among the bushes a twitter of lively birds exclaimed upon me. Finches went leaping past in bright flashes, and a robin sat and asked rudely: " Hello! Who are you?"

The bracken lay sere under the trees, broken and chavelled by the restless wild winds of the long winter.

The trees caught the wind in their tall netted twigs, and the young morning wind moaned at its captivity. As I trod the discarded oak-leaves and the bracken they uttered their last sharp gasps, pressed into oblivion. The wood was roofed with a wide young sobbing sound, and floored with a faint hiss like the intaking of the last breath. Between, was all the glad out-peeping of buds and anemone flowers and the rush of birds. I, wandering alone, felt them all, the anguish of the bracken fallen face-down in defeat, the careless dash of the birds, the sobbing of the young wind arrested in its haste, the trembling, expanding delight of the buds. I alone among them could hear the whole succession of chords.

The brooks talked on just the same, just as gladly, just as boisterously as they had done when I had netted small, glittering fish in the rest-pools. At Strelley Mill a servant girl in a white cap, and white apron-bands, came running out of the house with purple prayer-books, which she gave to the elder of two finicking girls who sat disconsolately with their black-silked mother in the governess cart at the gate ready to go to church. Near Woodside there was barbed-wire along the path, and at the end of every riding it was tarred on the tree-trunks, " Private."

* * *

The kitchen was a good-sized, low room that through long course of years had become absolutely a home. The great beams of the ceiling bowed easily, the chimney-seat had a bit of dark-green curtain, and under the high mantelpiece was another low shelf that the men could reach with their hands as they sat in the ingle-nook. There the pipes lay. Many generations of peaceful men and fruitful women had passed through the room, and not one but had added a new small comfort; a chair in the right place, a hook, a stool, a cushion, a certain pleasing cloth for the sofa covers, a shelf of books. The room, that looked so quiet and crude, was a home evolved through generations to fit the large bodies of the men who dwelled in it, and the placid fancy of the women. At last, it had an individuality. It was the home of the Renshaws, warm, lovable, serene. Emily was in perfect accord with its brownness, its shadows, its ease. I, as I sat on the sofa under the window, felt rejected by the kind room. I was distressed with a sense of ephemerality, of pale, erratic fragility.

* * *

Across the empty cornfield the partridges were running. We walked through the September haze slowly, because he was feeble on his legs. As he became tired he ceased to talk. We leaned for some time on a gate, in the brief glow of the transient afternoon, and he was stupid again. He did not notice the brown haste of the partridges, he did not care to share with me the handful of ripe blackberries, and when I pulled the bryony ropes off the hedges, and held the great knots of red and green berries in my hand, he glanced at them without interest or appreciation.

"Poison-berries, aren't they?" he said dully.

Like a tree that is falling, going soft and pale and rotten, clammy with small fungi, he stood leaning against the gate, while the dim afternoon drifted with a flow of thick sweet sunshine past him, not touching him.

In the stackyard, the summer's splendid monuments of wheat and grass were reared in gold and grey. The wheat was littered brightly round the rising stack. The loaded wagon clanked slowly up the incline, drew near, and rode like a ship at anchor against the scotches, brushing the stack with a crisp, sharp sound. Tom climbed the ladder and stood a moment there against the sky, amid the brightness and fragrance of the gold corn, and waved his arm to his wife who was passing in the shadow of the building. Then Arthur began to lift the sheaves to the stack, and the two men worked in an exquisite, subtle rhythm, their white sleeves and their dark heads gleaming, moving against the mild sky and the corn. The silence was broken only by the occasional lurch of the body of the wagon, as the teamer stepped to the front, or again to the rear of the load. Occasionally I could catch the blue glitter of the prongs of the forks. Tom, now lifted high above the small wagon-load, called to his brother some question about the stack. The sound of his voice was strong and mellow.

I turned to George, who also was watching, and said:

" You ought to be like that."

We heard Tom calling, " All right ! " and saw him standing high up on the tallest corner of the stack, as on the prow of a ship.

George watched, and his face slowly gathered expression. He turned to me, his dark eyes alive with horror and despair.

From *THE TRESPASSER*

Below, in the street, a military band passed glittering. A brave sound floated up, and again he laughed, loving the tune, the clash and glitter of the band, the movement of scarlet, blithe soldiers beyond the park. People were drifting brightly from church. How could it be Sunday ! It was no time ; it was Romance, going back to Tristan.

Women, like crocus-flowers, in white and blue and lavender, moved gaily. Everywhere fluttered the small flags of holiday. Every form danced lightly in the sunshine.

And beyond it all were the silent hillsides of the island, with Helena. It was so wonderful, he could bear to be patient. She would be all in white, with her cool, thick throat left bare to the breeze, her face shining, smiling as she dipped her head because of the sun, which glistened on her uncovered hair.

He breathed deeply, stirring at the thought. But he would not grow impatient. The train had halted over the town, where scarlet soldiers, and ludicrous blue sailors, and all the brilliant women from church shook like a kaleidoscope down the street. The train crawled on, drawing near to the sea, for which Siegmund waited breathless. It was so like Helena, blue, beautiful, strong in its reserve.

Another moment they were in the dirty station. Then the day flashed out, and Siegmund mated with joy. He felt the sea heaving below him. He looked round, and the sea was blue as a periwinkle flower, while gold and white and blood-red sails lit here and there upon the blueness. Standing on the deck, he gave himself to the breeze and to the sea, feeling like one of the ruddy sails—as if he were part of it all. All his body radiated amid the large, magnificent sea-moon like a piece of colour.

The little ship began to pulse, to tremble. White with the softness of a bosom, the water rose up frothing and swaying gently. Ships drew near like inquisitive birds ; the old *Victory* shook her myriad pointed flags of yellow and scarlet ; the straight old houses of the quay passed by.

Outside the harbour, like fierce creatures of the sea come wildly up to look, the battleships laid their black snouts on the water. Siegmund laughed at them. He felt the foam on his face like a sparkling, felt the blue sea gathering round.

On the left stood the round fortress, quaintly chequered, and solidly alone in the walk of water, amid the silent flight of the golden- and crimson-winged boats.

Siegmund watched the bluish bulk of the island. Like the beautiful women in the myths, his love hid in its blue haze. It seemed impossible. Behind him, the white wake trailed myriads of daisies. On either hand the grim and wicked battleships watched along their sharp noses. Beneath him the clear green water swung and puckered as if it were laughing. In front Sieglinde's island drew near and nearer, creeping towards him, bringing him Helena.

Meadows and woods appeared, houses crowded down to the shore to meet him; he was in the quay, and the ride was over. Siegmund regretted it. But Helena was on the island, which rode like an anchored ship under the fleets of cloud that had launched whilst Siegmund was on water. As he watched the end of the pier loom higher, large ponderous trains of cloud cast over him the shadows of their bulk, and he shivered in the chill wind.

* * *

He strode along, singing to himself, and spinning his towel rhythmically. A small path led him across a field down a zigzag in front of the cliffs. Some nooks, sheltered from the wind, were warm with sunshine, scented of honeysuckle and of thyme. He took a sprig of woodbine that was coloured of cream and butter. The grass wetted his brown shoes and his flannel trousers. Again, a fresh breeze put the scent of the sea in his uncovered hair. The cliff was a tangle of flowers above and below, with poppies at the lip being blown out like red flame, and scabious leaning inquisitively to look down, and pink and white rest-harrow everywhere, very pretty.

Siegmund stood at a bend where heath blossomed in shaggy lilac, where the sunshine but no wind came. He saw the blue bay curl away to the far-off headland. A few birds, white and small, circled, dipped by the thin foam-edge of the water; a few ships dimmed the sea with silent travelling; a few small people, dark or naked-white, moved below the swinging birds.

He chose his bathing-place where the incoming tide had half covered a stretch of fair, bright sand that was studded with rocks resembling square altars, hollowed on top. He threw his clothes on a high rock. It delighted him to feel the fresh, soft fingers of the wind touching him and wandering timidly over his nakedness. He ran laughing over the sand to the sea, where he waded in, thrusting his legs noisily through the heavy green water.

It was cold, and he shrank. For a moment he found himself thigh-deep, watching the horizontal stealing of a ship through the intolerable glitter, afraid to plunge. Laughing, he went under the clear green water.

He was a poor swimmer. Sometimes a choppy wave swamped him, and he rose gasping, wringing the water from his eyes and nostrils, while he heaved and sank with the rocking of the waves that clasped his breast. Then he stooped again to resume his game with the sea. It is splendid to play, even at middle age, and the sea is a fine partner.

With his eyes at the shining level of the water, he liked to peer across, taking a seal's view of the cliffs as they confronted the morning. He liked to see the ships standing up on a bright floor; he liked to see the birds come down.

But in his playing he drifted towards the spur of rock, where, as he swam, he caught his thigh on a sharp, submerged point. He frowned at the pain, at the sudden cruelty of the sea; then he thought no more of it, but ruffled his way back to the clear water, busily continuing his play.

When he ran out on to to the fair sand his heart, and brain, and body were in a turmoil. He panted, filling his breast with the air that was sparkled and tasted of the sea. As he shuddered a little, the wilful palpitation of his flesh pleased him, as if birds had fluttered against him. He offered his body to the morning, glowing with the sea's passion. The wind nestled in to him, the sunshine came on his shoulders like warm breath. He delighted in himself.

* * *

There was a shelving beach of warm white sand, bleached soft as velvet. A sounding of gulls filled the dark recesses of the headland; a low chatter of shingle came from where the easy water was breaking; a confused, shell-like murmur of the sea between the folded cliffs. Siegmund and Helena lay side by side upon the dry sand, small as two resting birds, while thousands of gulls whirled in a white-flaked storm above them, and the great cliffs towered beyond, and high up over the cliffs the multitudinous clouds were travelling, a vast caravan *en route*. Amidst the journeying of oceans and clouds and the circling flight of heavy spheres, lost to sight in the sky, Siegmund and Helena, two grains of life in the vast movement, were travelling a moment side by side.

They lay on the beach like a grey and a white sea-bird together. The lazy ships that were idling down the Solent observed the cliffs and the boulders, but Siegmund and Helena were too little. They lay ignored and insignificant, watching through half-closed fingers the diverse caravan of Day go past. They lay with their latticed fingers over their eyes, looking out at the sailing ships across their vision of blue water.

* * *

Siegmund had found a white cave welling with green water, brilliant and full of life as mounting sap. The white rock glimmered through the water, and soon Siegmund shimmered also in the living green of the sea, like pale flowers trembling upward.

"The water," said Siegmund, "is as full of life as I am," and he pressed forward his breast against it. He swam very well that morning; he had more wilful life than the sea, so he mastered it laughingly with his arms, feeling a delight in his triumph over the waves. Venturing recklessly in his new pride he swam round the corner of the rock, through an archway, lofty and spacious, into a passage where the water ran like a flood of green light over the skin-white bottom. Suddenly he emerged in the brilliant daylight of the next tiny scoop of a bay.

There he arrived like a pioneer, for the bay was inaccessible from the land. He waded out of the green, cold water on to sand that was pure as the shoulders of Helena, out of the shadow of the archway into the sunlight, on to the glistening petal of this blossom of a sea-bay.

He did not know till he felt the sunlight how the sea had drunk with its cold lips deeply of his warmth. Throwing himself down on the sand that was soft and warm as white fur, he lay glistening wet, panting, swelling with glad pride at having conquered also this small, inaccessible sea-cave, creeping into it like a white bee into a white virgin blossom that had waited, how long, for its bee.

The sand was warm to his breast, and his belly, and his arms. It was like a great body he cleaved to. Almost, he fancied, he felt it heaving under him in its breathing. Then he turned his face to the sun, and laughed. All the while, he hugged the warm body of the sea-bay beneath him. He spread his hands upon the sand; he took it in handfuls, and let it run smooth, warm, delightful, through his fingers.

"Surely," he said to himself, "it is like Helena"; and he laid his hands again on the warm body of the shore, let them wander, discovering, gathering all the warmth, the softness, the strange wonder of smooth warm pebbles, then shrinking from the deep weight of cold his hand encountered as he burrowed under the surface wrist-deep. In the end he found the cold mystery of the deep sand also thrilling. He pushed in his hands again and deeper, enjoying the almost hurt of the dark, heavy coldness. For the sun and the white flower of the bay were breathing and kissing him dry, were holding him in their warm concave, like a bee in a flower, like himself on the bosom of Helena, and flowing like the warmth of her breath in his hair came the sunshine, breathing near and lovingly: yet, under all, was this deep mass of cold, that the softness and warmth merely floated upon.

Siegmund lay and clasped the sand, and tossed it in handfuls till over him he was all hot and cloyed. Then he rose and looked at himself and laughed. The water was swaying reproachfully against the steep pebbles below, murmuring like a child that it was not fair—it was not fair he should abandon his playmate. Siegmund laughed, and began to rub himself free of the clogging sand. He found himself strangely dry and smooth. He tossed more dry sand, and more, over himself, busy and intent like a child playing some absorbing game with itself. Soon his body was dry and warm and smooth as a camomile flower. He was, however, greyed and smeared with sand-dust. Siegmund looked at himself with disapproval, though his body was full of delight and his hands glad with the touch of himself. He wanted himself clean. He felt the sand thick in his hair, even in his moustache. He went painfully over the pebbles till he found himself on the smooth rock bottom. Then he soused himself and shook his head in the water, and washed and splashed and rubbed himself with his hands assiduously. He must feel perfectly clean and free—fresh, as if he had washed away all the years of soilure in this morning's sea and sun and sand. It was the purification. Siegmund became again a happy priest of the sun. He felt as if all the dirt of misery were soaked out of him, as he might soak clean a soiled garment in the sea, and bleach it white in the sunny shore. So white and sweet and tissue-clean he felt—full of lightness and grace.

The garden in front of their house, where Helena was waiting for him, was long and crooked, with a sunken flagstone pavement running up to the door by the side of the lawn. On either hand the high fence of the garden was heavy with wild clematis and honeysuckle. Helena sat sideways, with a map spread out on her bench under the bushy little laburnum-tree, tracing the course of their wanderings. It was very still. There was just a murmur of bees going in and out the brilliant little porches of nasturtium flowers. The nasturtium leaf-coins stood cool and grey; in their delicate shade, underneath in the green twilight, a few flowers shone their submerged gold and scarlet. There was a faint scent of mignonette. Helena, like a white butterfly in the shade, her two white arms for antennæ stretching firmly to the bench, leaned over her map. She was busy, very busy, out of sheer happiness. She traced word after word, and evoked scene after scene. As she discovered a name, she conjured up the place. As she moved to the next mark she imagined the long path lifting and falling happily.

* * *

Then Siegmund forgot. He opened his eyes and saw the night about him. The moon had escaped from the cloud-pack, and was radiant behind a fine veil which glistened to her rays, and which was broidered with a lustrous halo, very large indeed, the largest halo Siegmund had ever seen. When the little lane turned full towards the moon, it seemed as if Siegmund and Helena would walk through a large Moorish arch of horseshoe shape, the enormous white halo opening in front of them. They walked on, keeping their faces to the moon, smiling with wonder and a little rapture, until once more the little lane curved wilfully, and they were walking north. Helena observed three cottages crouching under the hill and under trees to cover themselves from the magic of the moonlight.

"We certainly did not come this way before," she said triumphantly. The idea of being lost delighted her.

Siegmund looked round at the grey hills smeared over with a low, dim glisten of moon-mist. He could not yet fully realize that he was walking along a lane in the Isle of Wight. His surroundings seemed to belong to some state beyond ordinary experience—some place in romance, perhaps, or among the hills where Brünhild lay sleeping in her large bright halo of fire. How could it be that he and Helena were two children of London wandering to find their lodging in Freshwater? He sighed, and looked again over the hills where the moonlight was condensing in mist ethereal, frail, and yet substantial, reminding him of the way the manna must have condensed out of the white moonlit mists of Arabian deserts.

"We may be on the road to Newport," said Helena presently, "and the distance is ten miles."

She laughed, not caring in the least whither they wandered, exulting in this wonderful excursion! She and Siegmund alone in a glistening wilderness of night at the back of habited days and nights! Siegmund looked at her. He by no means shared her exultation, though he sympathized with it. He walked on alone in his deep seriousness, of which she was not aware. Yet when he noticed her abandon, he drew her nearer, and his heart softened with protecting tenderness towards her, and grew heavy with responsibility.

The fields breathed off a scent as if they were come to life with the night, and were talking with fragrant eagerness. The farms huddled together in sleep, and pulled the dark shadow over them to hide from the supernatural white night; the cottages were locked and darkened. Helena walked on in triumph through this wondrous hinterland of night, actively searching for the spirits, watching the cottages they approached, listening, looking for the dreams of those sleeping inside, in the darkened rooms. She imagined she could see the frail dream-faces at the windows; she fancied they stole out timidly into the gardens, and went running away among the rabbits on the gleamy hillside. Helena laughed to herself, pleased with her fancy of wayward little dreams playing with weak hands and feet among the large, solemn-sleeping cattle. This was the first time, she told herself, that she had ever been out among the grey-frocked dreams and white-armed fairies. She imagined herself lying asleep in her room, while her own dreams slid out down the moonbeams. She imagined Siegmund sleeping in his room, while his dreams, dark-eyed, their blue eyes very dark and yearning at night-time, came wandering over the grey grass seeking her dreams.

So she wove her fancies as she walked, until for very weariness she was fain to remember that it was a long way—a long way. Siegmund's arm was about her to support her; she rested herself upon it. They crossed a stile and recognized, on the right of the path, the graveyard of the Catholic chapel. The moon, which the days were paring smaller with envious keen knife, shone upon the white stones in the burial-ground. The carved Christ upon his cross hung against a silver-grey sky. Helena looked up wearily, bowing to the tragedy.

Siegmund also looked and bowed his head.

"Thirty years of earnest love; three years' life like a passionate ecstasy—and it was finished. He was very great and very wonderful. I am very insignificant, and shall go out ignobly. But we are the same; love, the brief ecstasy, and the end. But mine is one rose, and His all the white beauty in the world."

Siegmund felt his heart very heavy, sad, and at fault, in presence of the Christ. Yet he derived comfort from the knowledge that life was treating him in the same manner as it had treated the Master, though his compared small and despicable with the Christ-tragedy. Siegmund stepped softly into the shadow of the pine copse.

"Let me get under cover," he thought. "Let me hide in it; it is good, the sudden intense darkness. I am small and futile: my small, futile tragedy!"

* * *

In the midst of their passion of fear the moon rose. Siegmund started to see the rim appear ruddily beyond the sea. His struggling suddenly ceased, and he watched, spell-bound, the oval horn of fiery gold come up, resolve itself. Some golden liquor dripped and spilled upon the far waves, where it shook in ruddy splashes. The gold-red cup rose higher, looming before him very large, yet still not all discovered. By degrees the horn of gold detached itself from the darkness at back of the waves. It was immense and terrible. When would the tip be placed upon the table of the sea?

It stood at last, whole and calm, before him; then the night took up this drinking-cup of fiery gold, lifting it with majestic movement overhead, letting stream forth the wonderful unwasted liquor of gold over the sea—a libation.

Siegmund looked at the shaking flood of gold and paling gold spread wider as the night upraised the blanching crystal, poured out further and further the immense libation from the whitening cup, till at last the moon looked frail and empty.

And there, exhaustless in the night, the white light shook on the floor of the sea. He wondered how it would be gathered up. "I gather it up into myself," he said. And the stars and the cliffs and a few trees were watching, too. If I have spilled my life," he thought, "the unfamiliar eyes of the land and sky will gather it up again."

Turning to Helena, he found her face white and shining as the empty moon.

* * *

They wound through the pass of the South Downs. As Siegmund, looking backward, saw the northern slope of the Downs swooping smoothly, in a great, broad bosom of sward, down to the body of the land, he warmed with sudden love for the earth; there the great Downs were, naked like a breast, leaning kindly to him. The earth is always kind; it loves us, and would foster us like a nurse. The Downs were big and tender and simple. Siegmund looked at the farm, folded in a hollow, and he wondered what fortunate folk were there, nourished and quiet, hearing the vague roar of the train that was carrying him home.

Up towards Arundel the cornfields of red wheat were heavy with gold. It was evening, when the green of the trees went out, leaving dark shapes proud upon the sky; but the red wheat was forged in the sunset, hot and magnificent. Siegmund almost gloated as he smelled the ripe corn, and opened his eyes to its powerful radiation. For a moment he forgot everything amid the forging of red fields of gold in the smithy of the sunset. Like sparks, poppies blew along the railway banks, a crimson train. Siegmund waited, through the meadows, for the next wheat-field. It came like the lifting of yellow-hot metal out of the gloom of darkened grass-lands.

Helena was reassured by the glamour of evening over ripe Sussex. She breathed the land now and then, while she watched the sky. The sunset was stately. The blue-eyed day, with great limbs, having fought its victory and won, now mounted triumphant on its pyre, and with white arms uplifted took the flames, which leaped like blood about its feet. The day died nobly, so she thought.

One gold cloud, as an encouragement tossed to her, followed the train.

* * *

The streets were like polished gun-metal glistened over with gold. The taxi-cabs, the wild cats of the town, swept over the gleaming floor swiftly, soon lessening in the distance, as if scornful of the other clumsy-footed traffic. He heard the merry click-clock of the swinging hansoms, then the excited whirring of the motor-buses as they charged full-tilt heavily down the road, their hearts, as it seemed, beating with trepidation; they drew up with a sigh of relief by the kerb, and stood there panting—great, nervous, clumsy things. Siegmund was always amused by the headlong, floundering career of the buses. He was pleased with this scampering of the traffic; anything for distraction. He was glad Helena was not with him, for the streets would have irritated her with their coarse noise. She would stand for a long time to watch the rabbits pop and hobble along on the common at night; but the tearing along of the taxis and the charge of a great motor-bus was painful to her.

" Discords," she said, " after the trees and sea." She liked the glistening of the streets ; it seemed a fine alloy of gold laid down for pavement, such pavement as drew near to the pure gold streets of Heaven ; but this noise could not be endured near any wonderland.

Siegmund did not mind it ; it drummed out his own thoughts. He watched the gleaming magic of the road, raced over with shadows, project itself far before him into the night. He watched the people. Soldiers, belted with scarlet, went jauntily on in front. There was a peculiar charm in their movement. There was a soft vividness of life in their carriage ; it reminded Siegmund of the soft swaying and lapping of a poised candle-flame. The women went blithely alongside. Occasionally, in passing, one glanced at him ; then, in spite of himself, he smiled ; he knew not why. The women glanced at him with approval, for he was ruddy ; besides, he had that carelessness and abstraction of despair. The eyes of the women said : " You are comely, you are lovable," and Siegmund smiled.

When the street opened, at Westminster, he noticed the city sky, a lovely deep purple, and the lamps in the Square steaming out a vapour of grey-gold light.

" It is a wonderful night," he said to himself. " There are not two such in a year."

He went forward to the Embankment, with a feeling of elation in his heart. This purple and gold-grey world, with the fluttering flame-warmth of soldiers and the quick brightness of women, like lights that clip sharply in a draught, was a revelation to him.

As he leaned upon the Embankment parapet the wonder did not fade, but rather increased. The trams, one after another, floated loftily over the bridge. They went like great burning bees in an endless file into a hive past those which were drifting dreamily out, while below, on the black, distorted water, golden serpents flashed and twisted to and fro.

" Ah ! " said Siegmund to himself ; " it is far too wonderful for me. Here, as well as by the sea, the night is gorgeous and uncouth. Whatever happens, the world is wonderful."

So he went on amid all the vast miracle of movement in the

city night, the swirling of water to the sea, the gradual sweep of the stars, the floating of many lofty, luminous cars through the bridged darkness, like an army of angels filing past on one of God's campaigns, the purring haste of the taxis, the slightly dancing shadows of people. Siegmund went on slowly, like a slow bullet winging into the heart of life. He did not lose this sense of wonder, not in the train, nor as he walked home in the moonless dark.

* * *

He was awakened finally by his own perspiration. He was terribly hot. The pillow, the bedclothes, his hair, all seemed to be steaming with hot vapour, whilst his body was bathed in sweat. It was coming light. Immediately he shut his eyes again and lay still. He was now conscious, and his brain was irritably active, but his body was a separate thing, a terrible, heavy, hot thing over which he had slight control.

Siegmund lay still, with his eyes closed, enduring the exquisite torture of the trickling of drops of sweat. First it would be one gathering and running its irregular, hesitating way into the hollow of his neck. His every nerve thrilled to it, yet he felt he could not move more than to stiffen his throat slightly. While yet the nerves in the track of this drop were quivering, raw with sensitiveness, another drop would start from off the side of his chest, and trickle downwards among the little muscles of his side, to drip on to the bed. It was like the running of a spider over his sensitive, moveless body. Why he did not wipe himself he did not know. He lay still and endured this horrible tickling, which seemed to bite deep into him, rather than make the effort to move, which he loathed to do. The drops ran off his forehead down his temples. Those he did not mind: he was blunt there. But they started again, in tiny, vicious spurts, down the sides of his chest, from under his armpits, down the inner sides of his thighs, till he seemed to have a myriad quivering tracks of a myriad running insects over his hot, wet, highly-sensitized body. His nerves were trembling, one and all, with outrage and vivid suspense. It became unbearable. He felt that, if he endured it another moment, he would cry out, or suffocate and burst.

He sat up suddenly, threw away the bedclothes, from which came a puff of hot steam, and began to rub his pyjamas against his side and his legs. He rubbed madly for a few moments. Then he sighed with relief. He sat on the side of the bed, moving from the hot dampness of the place where he had lain. For a moment he thought he would go to sleep. Then, in an instant his brain seemed to click awake. He was still as loath as ever to move, but his brain was no longer clouded in hot vapour: it was clear. He sat, bowing forward on the side of the bed, his sleeping jacket open, the dawn stealing into the room, the morning air entering fresh through the wide-flung window-door. He felt a peculiar sense of guilt, of wrongness, in thus having jumped out of bed. It seemed to him as if he ought to have endured the heat of his body, and the infernal trickling of the drops of sweat. But at the thought of it he moved his hands gratefully over his sides, which now were dry, and soft, and smooth; slightly chilled on the surface perhaps, for he felt a sudden tremor of shivering from the warm contact of his hands.

Siegmund sat up straight: his body was re-animated. He felt the pillow and the groove where he had lain. It was quite wet and clammy. There was a scent of sweat on the bed not really unpleasant, but he wanted something fresh and cool.

Siegmund sat in the doorway that gave on to the small verandah. The air was beautifully cool. He felt his chest again to make sure it was not clammy. It was smooth as silk. This pleased him very much. He looked out on the night again, and was startled. Somewhere the moon was shining duskily, in a hidden quarter of sky; but straight in front of him, in the north-west, silent lightning was fluttering. He waited breathlessly to see if it were true. Then, again, the pale lightning jumped up into the dome of the fading night. It was like a white bird stirring restlessly on its nest. The night was drenching thinner, greyer. The lightning, like a bird that should have flown before the arm of day, moved on its nest in the boughs of darkness, raised itself, flickered its pale wings rapidly, then sank again, loath to fly. Siegmund watched it with wonder and delight.

The day was pushing aside the boughs of darkness, hunting. The poor moon would be caught when the net was flung. Siegmund went out on the balcony to look at it. There it was, like a poor white mouse, a half-moon, crouching on the mound of its course. It would run nimbly over to the western slope, then it would be caught in the net, and the sun would laugh, like a great yellow cat, as it stalked behind playing with its prey, flashing out its bright paws. The moon, before making its last run, lay crouched, palpitating. The sun crept forth, laughing to itself as it saw its prey could not escape. The lightning, however, leaped low off the nest like a bird decided to go, and flew away. Siegmund no longer saw it opening and shutting its wings in hesitation amid the disturbance of the dawn. Instead there came a flush, the white lightning gone. The brief pink butterflies of sunrise and sunset rose up from the mown fields of darkness, and fluttered low in a cloud. Even in the west, they flew in a narrow, rosy swarm. They separated, thinned, rising higher. Some, flying up, became golden. Some flew rosy gold across the moon, the mouse-moon motionless with fear. Soon the pink butterflies had gone, leaving a scarlet stretch like a field of poppies in the fens. As a wind, the light of day blew in from the east, puff after puff filling with whiteness the space which had been the night. Siegmund sat watching the last morning blowing in across the mown darkness, till the whole field of the world was exposed, till the moon was like a dead mouse which floats on water.

From *SONS AND LOVERS*

" The Bottoms " succeeded to " Hell Row." Hell Row was a block of thatched, bulging cottages that stood by the brookside on Greenhill Lane. There lived the colliers who worked in the little gin-pits two fields away. The brook ran under the alder-trees, scarcely soiled by these small mines, whose coal was drawn to the surface by donkeys that plodded wearily in a circle round a gin. And all over the countryside were these same pits, some of which had been worked in the time of Charles II, the few colliers and the donkeys burrowing down like ants into the earth, making queer mounds and little black places among the corn-fields and the meadows. And the cottages of these coalminers, in blocks and pairs here and there, together with odd farms and homes of the stockingers, straying over the parish, formed the village of Bestwood.

Then, some sixty years ago, a sudden change took place. The gin-pits were elbowed aside by the large mines of the financiers. The coal and iron field of Nottinghamshire and Derbyshire was discovered. Carston, Waite and Co. appeared. Amid tremendous excitement, Lord Palmerstone formally opened the company's first mine at Spinney Park, on the edge of Sherwood Forest.

About this time the notorious Hell Row, which through growing old had acquired an evil reputation, was burned down, and much dirt was cleansed away.

Carston, Waite and Co. found they had struck on a good thing, so, down the valleys of the brooks from Selby and Nuttall, new mines were sunk, until soon there were six pits working. From Nuttall, high up on the sandstone among the woods, the railway ran, past the ruined priory of the Carthusians and past Robin Hood's Well, down to Spinney Park, then on to Minton, a large mine among corn-fields; from Minton across the farm-lands of the valleyside to Bunker's Hill, branching off there, and running north to Beggarlee and Selby, that looks over at Crich and the hills of Derbyshire; six mines like black studs on the countryside, linked by a loop of fine chain, the railway.

To accommodate the regiments of miners, Carston, Waite and Co. built the Squares, great quadrangles of dwellings on the hillside of Bestwood, and then, in the brook valley, on the site of Hell Row, they erected the Bottoms.

The Bottoms consisted of six blocks of miners' dwellings, two rows of three, like the dots on a blank-six domino, and twelve houses in a block. This double row of dwellings sat at the foot of the rather sharp slope from Bestwood, and looked out, from the attic windows at least, on the slow climb of the valley towards Selby.

The houses themselves were substantial and very decent. One could walk all round, seeing little front gardens with auriculas and saxifrage in the shadow of the bottom block, sweet-williams and pinks in the sunny top block; seeing neat front windows, little porches, little privet hedges, and dormer windows for the attics. But that was outside; that was the view on to the uninhabited parlours of all the colliers' wives. The dwelling-room, the kitchen, was at the back of the house, facing inward between the blocks, looking at a scrubby back garden, and then at the ash-pits. And between the rows, between the long lines of ash-pits, went the alley, where the children played and the women gossiped and the men smoked. So the actual conditions of living in the Bottoms, that was so well built and that looked so nice, were quite unsavoury because people must live in the kitchen, and the kitchens opened on to that nasty alley of ash-pits.

* * *

Mrs. Morel did not like the wakes. There were two sets of horses, one going by steam, one pulled round by a pony; three organs were grinding, and there came odd cracks of pistol-shots, fearful screeching of the cocoa-nut man's rattle, shouts of the Aunt Sally man, screeches from the peep-show lady. The mother perceived her son gazing enraptured outside the Lion Wallace booth, at the pictures of this famous lion that had killed a negro and maimed for life two white men. She left him alone, and went to get Annie a spin of toffee. Presently the lad stood in front of her, wildly excited.

"You never said you was coming—isn't the' a lot of things?—that lion's killed three men—I've spent my tuppence—an' look here."

He pulled from his pocket two egg-cups, with pink moss-roses on them.

"I got these from that stall where y'ave ter get them marbles in them holes. An' I got these two in two goes—'aepenny a go—they've got moss-roses on, look here. I wanted these."

She knew he wanted them for her.

"H'm!" she said, pleased. "They *are* pretty!"

"Shall you carry 'em, 'cause I'm frightened o' breakin' 'em?"

He was tipful of excitement now she had come, led her about the ground, showed her everything. Then, at the peep-show she explained the pictures, in a sort of story, to which he listened as if spellbound. He would not leave her. All the time he stuck close to her, bristling with a small boy's pride of her. For no other woman looked such a lady as she did, in her little black bonnet and her cloak. She smiled when she saw women she knew. When she was tired she said to her son:

"Well, are you coming now, or later?"

"Are you goin' a'ready?" he cried, his face full of reproach.

"Already? It is past four, *I* know."

"What are you goin' a'ready for?" he lamented.

"You needn't come if you don't want," she said.

And she went slowly away with her little girl, whilst her son stood watching her, cut to the heart to let her go, and yet unable to leave the wakes. As she crossed the open ground in front of the "Moon and Stars" she heard men shouting, and smelled the beer, and hurried a little, thinking her husband was probably in the bar.

* * *

The moon was high and magnificent in the August night. Mrs. Morel, seared with passion, shivered to find herself out there in a great white light, that fell cold on her, and gave a shock to her inflamed soul. She stood for a few moments helplessly staring at the glistening great rhubarb leaves near the door. Then she got the air into her breast. She walked down the garden path, trembling in every limb, while the child boiled within her. For a while she could not control her consciousness; mechanically she went over the last scene, then over it again, certain phrases, certain moments coming each time like a brand red-hot down on her soul; and each time she enacted again the past hour, each time the brand came down at the same points, till the mark was burnt in, and the pain burnt out, and at last she came to herself. She must have been half an hour in this delirious condition. Then the presence of the night came again to her. She glanced round in fear. She had wandered to the side garden, where she was walking up and down the path beside the currant bushes under the long wall. The garden was a narrow strip, bounded from the road, that cut transversely between the blocks, by a thick thorn hedge.

She hurried out of the side garden to the front, where she could stand as if in an immense gulf of white light, the moon streaming high in face of her, the moonlight standing up from the hills in front, and filling the valley where the Bottoms crouched, almost blindingly. There, panting and half-weeping in reaction from the stress, she murmured to herself over and over again: "The nuisance! the nuisance!"

She became aware of something about her. With an effort she roused herself to see what it was that penetrated her consciousness. The tall white lilies were reeling in the moonlight, and the air was charged with their perfume, as with a presence. Mrs. Morel gasped slightly in fear. She touched the big, pallid flowers on their petals, then shivered. They seemed to be stretching in the moonlight. She put her hand into one white bin; the gold scarcely showed on her fingers by moonlight. She bent down to look at the binful of yellow pollen; but it only appeared dusky. Then she drank a deep draught of the scent. It almost made her dizzy.

Mrs. Morel leaned on the garden gate, looking out, and she lost herself awhile. She did not know what she thought. Except for a slight feeling of sickness, and her consciousness in the child, herself melted out like scent into the shiny, pale air. After a time the child, too, melted with her in the mixing-pot of moonlight, and she rested with the hills and lilies and houses all swum together in a kind of swoon.

When she came to herself she was tired for sleep. Languidly she looked about her; the clumps of white phlox seemed like bushes spread with linen; a moth ricocheted over them, and right across the garden. Following it with her eye roused her. A few whiffs of the raw, strong scent of phlox invigorated her.

She passed along the path, hesitating at the white rose-bush. It smelled sweet and simple. She touched the white ruffles of the roses. Their fresh scent and cool, soft leaves reminded her of the morning-time and sunshine. She was very fond of them. But she was tired, and wanted to sleep. In the mysterious out-of-doors she felt forlorn.

There was no noise anywhere. Evidently the children had not been wakened, or had gone to sleep again. A train, three miles away, roared across the valley. The night was very large, and very strange, stretching its hoary distances infinitely. And out of the silver-grey fog of darkness came sounds vague and hoarse: a corncrake not far off, sound of a train like a sigh, and distant shouts of men.

* * *

He always made his own breakfast. Being a man who rose early and had plenty of time he did not, as some miners do, drag his wife out of bed at six o'clock. At five, sometimes earlier, he woke, got straight out of bed, and went downstairs. When she could not sleep, his wife lay waiting for this time as for a period of peace. The only real rest seemed to be when he was out of the house.

He went downstairs in his shirt and then struggled into his pit-trousers, which were left on the hearth to warm all night. There was always a fire, because Mrs. Morel raked. And the first sound in the house was the bang, bang of the poker against the raker, as Morel smashed the remainder of the coal to make the kettle, which was filled and left on the hob, finally boil. His cup and knife and fork, all he wanted except just the food, was laid ready on the table on a newspaper. Then he got his breakfast, made the tea, packed the bottom of the doors with rugs to shut out the draught, piled a big fire, and sat down to an hour of joy. He toasted his bacon on a fork and caught the drops of fat on his bread; then he put the rasher on his thick slice of bread, and cut off chunks with a clasp-knife, poured his tea into his saucer, and was happy. With his family about, meals were never so pleasant. He loathed a fork; it is a modern introduction which has still scarcely reached common people.

What Morel preferred was a clasp-knife. Then, in solitude, he ate and drank, often sitting, in cold weather, on a little stool with his back to the warm chimney-piece, his food on the fender, his cup on the hearth. And then he read the last night's newspaper—what of it he could—spelling it over laboriously. He preferred to keep the blinds down and the candle lit even when it was daylight; it was the habit of the mine.

At a quarter to six he rose, cut two thick slices of bread-and-butter, and put them in the white calico snap-bag. He filled his tin bottle with tea. Cold tea without milk or sugar was the drink he preferred for the pit. Then he pulled off his shirt, and put on his pit-singlet, a vest of thick flannel cut low round the neck, and with short sleeves like a chemise.

Then he went upstairs to his wife with a cup of tea because she was ill, and because it occurred to him.

* * *

She went over the sheep-bridge and across a corner of the meadow to the cricket-ground. The meadows seemed one space of ripe, evening light, whispering with the distant mill-race. She sat on a seat under the alders in the cricket-ground, and fronted the evening. Before her, level and solid, spread the big green cricket-field, like the bed of a sea of light. Children played in the bluish shadow of the pavilion. Many rooks, high up, came cawing home across the softly-woven sky. They stooped in a long curve down into the golden glow, concentrating, cawing, wheeling, like black flakes on a slow vortex, over a tree-clump that made a dark boss among the pasture.

A few gentlemen were practising, and Mrs. Morel could hear the chock of the ball, and the voices of the men suddenly roused; could see the white forms of men shifting silently over the green upon which already the under-shadows were smouldering. Away at the grange, one side of the haystacks was lit up, the other sides blue-grey. A wagon of sheaves rocked small across the melting yellow light.

The sun was going down. Every open evening, the hills of Derbyshire were blazed over with red sunset. Mrs. Morel watched the sun sink from the glistening sky, leaving a soft flower-blue overhead, while the western space went red, as if all the fire had swum down there, leaving the bell cast flawless blue. The mountain-ash berries across the field stood fierily out from the dark leaves, for a moment. A few shocks of corn in a corner of the fallow stood up as if alive; she imagined them bowing; perhaps her son would be a Joseph. In the east, a mirrored sunset floated pink opposite the west's scarlet. The big haystacks on the hillside, that butted into the glare, went cold.

With Mrs. Morel it was one of those still moments when the small frets vanish, and the beauty of things stands out, and she had the peace and the strength to see herself. Now and again, a swallow cut close to her. Now and again, Annie came up with a handful of alder-currants. The baby was restless on his mother's knee, clambering with his hands at the light.

* * *

Annie and Paul and Arthur loved the winter evenings, when it was not wet. They stayed indoors till the colliers were all gone home, till it was thick dark, and the street would be deserted. Then they tied their scarves round their necks, for they scorned overcoats, as all the colliers' children did, and went out. The entry was very dark, and at the end the whole great night opened out, in a hollow, with a little tangle of lights below where Minton pit lay, and another far away opposite for Selby. The farthest tiny lights seemed to stretch out the darkness for ever. The children looked anxiously down the road at the one lamp-post, which stood at the end of the field path. If the little luminous space were deserted, the two boys felt genuine desolation. They stood with their hands in their pockets under the lamp, turning their backs on the night, quite miserable, watching the dark houses. Suddenly a pinafore under a short coat was seen, and a long-legged girl came flying up.

"Where's Billy Pillins an' your Annie an' Eddie Dakin?"

"I don't know."

But it did not matter so much—there were three now. They set up a game round the lamp-post, till the others rushed up, yelling. Then the play went fast and furious.

There was only this one lamp-post. Behind was the great scoop of darkness, as if all the night were there. In front, another wide, dark way opened over the hill brow. Occasionally somebody came out of this way and went into the field down the path. In a dozen yards the night had swallowed them. The children played on.

They were brought exceedingly close together owing to their isolation. If a quarrel took place, the whole play was spoilt. Arthur was very touchy, and Billy Pillins—really Philips—was worse. Then Paul had to side with Arthur, and on Paul's side went Alice, while Billy Pillins always had Emmie Limb and Eddie Dakin to back him up. Then the six would fight, hate with a fury of hatred, and flee home in terror. Paul never forgot, after one of these fierce internecine fights, seeing a big red moon lift itself up, slowly, between the waste road over the hill-top, steadily, like a great bird. And he thought of the Bible, that the moon should be turned to blood. And the next day he made haste to be friends with Billy Pillins. And then the wild, intense games went on again under the lamp-post, surrounded by so much darkness. Mrs. Morel, going into her parlour, would hear the children singing away:

"My shoes are made of Spanish leather,
  My socks are made of silk;
I wear a ring on every finger,
  I wash myself in milk."

They sounded so perfectly absorbed in the game as their voices came out of the night, that they had the feel of wild creatures singing. It stirred the mother; and she understood when they came in at eight o'clock, ruddy, with brilliant eyes, and quick, passionate speech.

* * *

And then, at ten o'clock, he set off. He was supposed to be a queer, quiet child. Going up the sunny street of the little town, he felt as if all the folk he met said to themselves: "He's going to the Co-op reading-room to look in the papers for a place. He can't get a job. I suppose he's living on his mother." Then he crept up the stone stairs behind the drapery shop at the

Co-op, and peeped in the reading-room. Usually one or two men were there, either old, useless fellows, or colliers "on the club." So he entered, full of shrinking and suffering when they looked up, seated himself at the table, and pretended to scan the news. He knew they would think, "What does a lad of thirteen want in a reading-room with a newspaper?" and he suffered.

Then he looked wistfully out of the window. Already he was a prisoner of industrialism. Large sunflowers stared over the old red wall of the garden opposite, looking in their jolly way down on the women who were hurrying with something for dinner. The valley was full of corn, brightening in the sun. Two collieries, among the fields, waved their small white plumes of steam. Far off on the hills were the woods of Annesley, dark and fascinating. Already his heart went down. He was being taken into bondage. His freedom in the beloved home valley was going now.

The brewers' wagons came rolling up from Keston with enormous barrels, four a side, like beans in a burst bean-pod. The wagoner, throned aloft, rolling massively in his seat, was not so much below Paul's eye. The man's hair, on his small, bullet head, was bleached almost white by the sun and on his thick red arms, rocking idly on his sack apron, the white hairs glistened. His red face shone and was almost asleep with sunshine. The horses, handsome and brown, went on by themselves, looking by far the masters of the show.

Paul wished he were stupid. "I wish," he thought to himself, "I was fat like him, and like a dog in the sun. I wish I was a pig and a brewer's wagoner."

* * *

From the train going home at night he used to watch the lights of the town, sprinkled thick on the hills, fusing together in a blaze in the valleys. He felt rich in life and happy. Drawing farther off, there was a patch of lights at Bulwell like myriad petals shaken to the ground from the shed stars; and beyond was the red glare of the furnaces, playing like hot breath on the clouds.

He had to walk two or more miles from Keston home, up

two long hills, down two short hills. He was often tired, and he counted the lamps climbing the hill above him, how many more to pass. And from the hilltop, on pitch-dark nights, he looked round on the villages five or six miles away, that shone like swarms of glittering living things, almost a heaven against his feet. Marlpool and Heanor scattered the far-off darkness with brilliance. And occasionally the black valley space between was traced, violated by a great train rushing south to London or north to Scotland. The trains roared by like projectiles level on the darkness, fuming and burning, making the valley clang with their passage. They were gone, and the lights of the towns and villages glittered in silence.

* * *

Miriam was moving about preparing dinner. Paul watched everything that happened. His face was pale and thin, but his eyes were quick and bright with life as ever. He watched the strange, almost rhapsodic way in which the girl moved about, carrying a great stew-jar to the oven, or looking in the saucepan. The atmosphere was different from that of his own home, where everything seemed so ordinary. When Mr. Leivers called loudly outside to the horse, that was reaching over to feed on the rose-bushes in the garden, the girl started, looked round with dark eyes, as if something had come breaking in on her world. There was a sense of silence inside the house and out. Miriam seemed as in some dreamy tale, a maiden in bondage, her spirit dreaming in a land far away and magical. And her discoloured old blue frock and her broken boots seemed only like the romantic rags of King Cophetua's beggar-maid.

She suddenly became aware of his keen blue eyes upon her, taking her all in. Instantly her broken boots and her frayed old frock hurt her. She resented his seeing everything. Even he knew that her stocking was not pulled up. She went into the scullery, blushing deeply. And afterwards her hands trembled slightly at her work. She nearly dropped all she handled. When her inside dream was shaken, her body quivered with trepidation. She resented that he saw so much.

* * *

She wanted to show him a certain wild-rose bush she had discovered. She knew it was wonderful. And yet, till he had seen it, she felt it had not come into her soul. Only he could make it her own, immortal. She was dissatisfied.

Dew was already on the paths. In the old oak-wood a mist was rising, and he hesitated, wondering whether one whiteness were a strand of fog or only campion-flowers pallid in a cloud.

By the time they came to the pine-trees Miriam was getting very eager and very tense. Her bush might be gone. She might not be able to find it; and she wanted it so much. Almost passionately she wanted to be with him when he stood before the flowers. They were going to have a communion together—something that thrilled her, something holy. He was walking beside her in silence. They were very near to each other. She trembled, and he listened, vaguely anxious.

Coming to the edge of the wood, they saw the sky in front, like mother-of-pearl, and the earth growing dark. Somewhere on the outermost branches of the pinewood the honeysuckle was streaming scent.

"Where?" he asked.

"Down the middle path," she murmured, quivering.

When they turned the corner of the path she stood still. In the wide walk between the pines, gazing rather frightened, she could distinguish nothing for some moments; the greying light robbed things of their colour. Then she saw her bush.

"Ah!" she cried, hastening forward.

It was very still. The tree was tall and straggling. It had thrown its briers over a hawthorn-bush, and its long streamers trailed thick, right down to the grass, splashing the darkness everywhere with great spilt stars, pure white. In bosses of ivory and in large splashed stars the roses gleamed on the darkness of foliage and stems and grass. Paul and Miriam stood close together, silent, and watched. Point after point the steady roses shone out to them, seeming to kindle something in their souls. The dusk came like smoke around, and still did not put out the roses.

Paul looked into Miriam's eyes. She was pale and expectant with wonder, her lips were parted, and her dark eyes lay open to him. His look seemed to travel down into her. Her soul quivered. It was the communion she wanted. He turned aside, as if pained. He turned to the bush.

"They seem as if they walk like butterflies, and shake themselves," he said.

She looked at her roses. They were white, some incurved and holy, others expanded in an ecstasy. The tree was dark as a shadow. She lifted her hand impulsively to the flowers; she went forward and touched them in worship.

"Let us go," he said.

* * *

On the Easter Monday the same party took an excursion to Wingfield Manor. It was great excitement to Miriam to catch a train at Sethley Bridge, amid all the bustle of the Bank Holiday crowd. They left the train at Alfreton. Paul was interested in the street and in the colliers with their dogs. Here was a new race of miners. Miriam did not live till they came to the church. They were all rather timid of entering, with their bags of food, for fear of being turned out. Leonard, a comic, thin fellow, went first; Paul, who would have died rather than be sent back, went last. The place was decorated for Easter. In the font hundreds of white narcissi seemed to be growing. The air was dim and coloured from the windows, and thrilled with a subtle scent of lilies and narcissi. In that atmosphere Miriam's soul came into a glow. Paul was afraid of the things he mustn't do; and he was sensitive to the feel of the place. Miriam turned to him. He answered. They were together. He would not go beyond the Communion-rail. She loved him for that. Her soul expanded into prayer beside him. He felt the strange fascination of shadowy religious places. All his latent mysticism quivered into life. She was drawn to him. He was a prayer along with her.

Miriam very rarely talked to the other lads. They at once became awkward in conversation with her. So usually she was silent.

It was past midday when they climbed the steep path to the manor. All things shone softly in the sun, which was wonderfully warm and enlivening. Celandines and violets were out.

Everybody was tip-top full with happiness. The glitter of the ivy, the soft, atmospheric grey of the castle walls, the gentleness of everything near the ruin, was perfect.

The manor is of hard, pale grey stone, and the outer walls are blank and calm. The young folk were in raptures. They went in trepidation, almost afraid that the delight of exploring this ruin might be denied them. In the first courtyard, within the high broken walls, were farm-carts, with their shafts lying idle on the ground, the tyres of the wheels brilliant with gold-red rust. It was very still.

All eagerly paid their sixpences, and went timidly through the fine clean arch of the inner courtyard. They were shy. Here on the pavement, where the hall had been, an old thorn-tree was budding. All kinds of strange openings and broken rooms were in the shadow around them.

* * *

They were now in the bare country of stone walls, which he loved, and which, though only ten miles from home, seemed so foreign to Miriam. The party was straggling. As they were crossing a large meadow that sloped away from the sun, along a path embedded with innumerable tiny glittering points, Paul, walking alongside, laced his fingers in the strings of the bag Miriam was carrying, and instantly she felt Annie behind, watchful and jealous. But the meadow was bathed in a glory of sunshine, and the path was jewelled, and it was seldom that he gave her any sign. She held her fingers very still among the strings of the bag, his fingers touching; and the place was golden as a vision.

At last they came into the straggling grey village of Crich, that lies high. Beyond the village was the famous Crich Stand that Paul could see from the garden at home. The party pushed on. Great expanse of country spread around and below. The lads were eager to get to the top of the hill. It was capped by a round knoll, half of which was by now cut away, and on the top of which stood an ancient monument, sturdy and squat, for signalling in old days far down into the level lands of Nottinghamshire and Leicestershire.

It was blowing so hard, high up there in the exposed place, that the only way to be safe was to stand nailed by the wind to the wall of the tower. At their feet fell the precipice where the limestone was quarried away. Below was a jumble of hills and tiny villages—Matlock, Ambergate, Stoney Middleton. The lads were eager to spy out the church of Bestwood, far away among the rather crowded country on the left. They were disgusted that it seemed to stand on a plain. They saw the hills of Derbyshire fall into the monotony of the Midlands that swept away South.

Miriam was somewhat scared by the wind, but the lads enjoyed it. They went on, miles and miles, to Whatstandwell. All the food was eaten, everybody was hungry, and there was very little money to get home with. But they managed to procure a loaf and a currant-loaf, which they hacked into pieces with shut-knives, and ate sitting on the wall near the bridge, watching the bright Derwent rushing by, and the brakes from Matlock pulling up at the inn.

* * *

One evening he and she went up the great sweeping shore of sand towards Theddlethorpe. The long breakers plunged and ran in a hiss of foam along the coast. It was a warm evening. There was not a figure but themselves on the far reaches of sand, no noise but the sound of the sea. Paul loved to see it clanging at the land. He loved to feel himself between the noise of it and the silence of the sandy shore. Miriam was with him. Everything grew very intense. It was quite dark when they turned again. The way home was through a gap in the sandhills, and then along a raised grass road between two dykes. The country was black and still. From behind the sandhills came the whisper of the sea. Paul and Miriam walked in silence. Suddenly he started. The whole of his blood seemed to burst into flame, and he could scarcely breathe. An enormous orange moon was staring at them from the rim of the sandhills. He stood still, looking at it.

"Ah!" cried Miriam, when she saw it.

He remained perfectly still, staring at the immense and ruddy moon, the only thing in the far-reaching darkness of the level. His heart beat heavily, the muscles of his arms contracted.

"What is it?" murmured Miriam, waiting for him.

He turned and looked at her. She stood beside him, for ever in shadow. Her face, covered with the darkness of her hat, was watching him unseen. But she was brooding. She was slightly afraid—deeply moved and religious. That was her best state. He was impotent against it. His blood was concentrated like a flame in his chest. But he could not get across to her. There were flashes in his blood. But somehow she ignored them. She was expecting some religious state in him. Still yearning, she was half aware of his passion, and gazed at him, troubled.

* * *

One evening about this time he had walked along the home road with her. They stood by the pasture leading down to the wood, unable to part. As the stars came out the clouds closed. They had glimpses of their own constellation, Orion, towards the west. His jewels glimmered for a moment, his dog ran low, struggling with difficulty through the spume of cloud.

Orion was for them chief in significance among the constellations. They had gazed at him in their strange, surcharged hours of feeling, until they seemed themselves to live in every one of his stars. This evening Paul had been moody and perverse. Orion had seemed just an ordinary constellation to him. He had fought against his glamour and fascination. Miriam was watching her lover's mood carefully. But he said nothing that gave him away, till the moment came to part, when he stood frowning gloomily at the gathered clouds, behind which the great constellation must be striding still.

* * *

At this time he gave all his friendship to Edgar. He loved the family so much, he loved the farm so much; it was the dearest place on earth to him. His home was not so lovable. It was his mother. But then he would have been just as happy with his mother anywhere. Whereas Willey Farm he loved passionately. He loved the little pokey kitchen, where men's boots tramped, and the dog slept with one eye open for fear of being trodden on; where the lamp hung over the table at night, and everything was so silent. He loved Miriam's long, low parlour, with its atmosphere of romance, its flowers, its books, its high, rosewood piano. He loved the gardens and the buildings that stood with their scarlet roofs on the naked edges of the fields, crept towards the wood as if for cosiness, the wild country scooping down a valley and up the uncultured hills of the other side. Only to be there was an exhilaration and a joy to him. He loved Mrs. Leivers, with her unworldliness and her quaint cynicism; he loved Mr. Leivers, so warm and young and lovable; he loved Edgar, who lit up when he came, and the boys and the children and Bill—even the sow Circe and the Indian game-cock called Tippoo. All this besides Miriam. He could not give it up.

* * *

They found at the top of the hill a hidden wild field, two sides of which were backed by the wood, the other sides by high loose hedges of hawthorn and elder-bushes. Between these overgrown bushes were gaps that the cattle might have walked through had there been any cattle now. There the turf was smooth as velveteen, padded and holed by the rabbits. The field itself was coarse, and crowded with tall, big cowslips that had never been cut. Clusters of strong flowers rose everywhere above the coarse tussocks of bent. It was like a roadstead crowded with tall, fairy shipping.

"Ah!" cried Miriam, and she looked at Paul, her dark eyes dilating. He smiled. Together they enjoyed the field of flowers. Clara, a little way off, was looking at the cowslips disconsolately. Paul and Miriam stayed close together, talking in subdued tones. He kneeled on one knee, quickly gathering the best blossoms, moving from tuft to tuft, restlessly, talking softly all the time. Miriam plucked the flowers lovingly, lingering over them. He always seemed to her too quick and almost scientific. Yet his bunches had a natural beauty more than hers. He loved them, but as if they were his and he had a right to them. She had more reverence for them: they held something she had not.

The flowers were very fresh and sweet. He wanted to drink them. As he gathered them, he ate the little yellow trumpets.

* * *

The Castle grounds were very green and fresh. Climbing the precipitous ascent he laughed and chattered, but she was silent, seeming to brood over something. There was scarcely time to go inside the squat, square building that crowns the bluff of rock. They leaned upon the wall where the cliff runs sheer down to the Park. Below them, in their holes in the sandstone, pigeons preened themselves and cooed softly. Away down the boulevard at the foot of the rock, tiny trees stood in their own pools of shadow, and tiny people went scurrying about in almost ludicrous importance.

"You feel as if you could scoop up the folk like tadpoles, and have a handful of them," he said.

She laughed, answering:

"Yes; it is not necessary to get far off in order to see us proportionately. The trees are much more significant."

"Bulk only," he said.

She laughed cynically.

Away beyond the boulevard the thin stripes of the metals showed upon the railway track, whose margin was crowded with little stacks of timber, beside which smoking toy engines fussed. Then the silver string of the canal lay at random among the black heaps. Beyond, the dwellings, very dense on the river flat, looked like black, poisonous herbage, in thick rows and crowded beds, stretching away, broken now and then by taller plants, right to where the river glistened in a hieroglyph across the country. The steep scarp cliffs across the river looked puny. Great stretches of country darkened with trees and faintly brightened with cornland, spread towards the haze, where the hills rose blue beyond grey.

"It is comforting," said Mrs. Dawes, "to think the town goes no farther. It is only a *little* sore upon the country yet."

"A little scab," Paul said.

She shivered. She loathed the town. Looking drearily across at the country which was forbidden her, her impassive face pale and hostile, she reminded Paul of one of the bitter, remorseful angels.

"But the town's all right," he said; "it's only temporary. This is the crude, clumsy make-shift we've practised on, till we find out what the idea is. The town will come all right."

* * *

There was a great crop of cherries at the farm. The trees at the back of the house, very large and tall, hung thick with scarlet and crimson drops, under the dark leaves. Paul and Edgar were gathering the fruit one evening. It had been a hot day, and now the clouds were rolling in the sky, dark and warm. Paul climbed high in the tree, above the scarlet roofs of the buildings. The wind, moaning steadily, made the whole tree rock with a subtle, thrilling motion that stirred the blood. The young man, perched insecurely in the slender branches rocked till he felt slightly drunk, reached down the boughs, where the scarlet beady cherries hung thick underneath, and tore off handful after handful of the sleek, cool-fleshed fruit. Cherries touched his ears and his neck as he stretched forward, their chill finger-tips sending a flash down his blood. All shades of red, from a golden vermilion to a rich crimson, glowed and met his eyes under a darkness of leaves.

The sun, going down, suddenly caught the broken clouds. Immense piles of gold flared out in the south-east, heaped in soft, glowing yellow right up the sky. The world, till now dusk and grey, reflected the gold glow, astonished. Everywhere the trees and the grass, and the far-off water, seemed roused from the twilight and shining.

* * *

He got to the cottage at about eleven o'clock. Miriam was busy preparing dinner. She looked so perfectly in keeping with the little kitchen, ruddy and busy. He kissed her and sat down to watch. The room was small and cosy. The sofa was covered all over with a sort of linen in squares of red and pale blue, old, much washed, but pretty. There was a stuffed owl in a case over a corner cupboard. The sunlight came through the leaves of the scented geraniums in the window. She was cooking a chicken in his honour. It was their cottage for the day, and they were man and wife. He beat the eggs for her and peeled the potatoes. He thought she gave a feeling of home almost like his mother; and no one could look more beautiful, with her tumbled curls, when she was flushed from the fire.

The dinner was a great success. Like a young husband, he carved. They talked all the time with unflagging zest. Then he wiped the dishes she had washed, and they went out down the fields. There was a bright little brook that ran into a bog at the foot of a very steep bank. Here they wandered, picking still a few marsh-marigolds and many big blue forget-me-nots. Then she sat on the bank with her hands full of flowers, mostly golden water-blobs. As she put her face down into the marigolds, it was all overcast with a yellow shine.

"Your face is bright," he said, "like a transfiguration."

She looked at him, questioning. He laughed pleadingly to her, laying his hand on hers. Then he kissed her fingers, then her face.

The world was all steeped in sunshine, and quite still, yet not asleep, but quivering with a kind of expectancy.

* * *

It grew late. Through the open door, stealthily, came the scent of madonna lilies, almost as if it were prowling abroad. Suddenly he got up and went out of doors.

The beauty of the night made him want to shout. A half-moon, dusky gold, was sinking behind the black sycamore at the end of the garden, making the sky dull purple with its glow. Nearer, a dim white fence of lilies went across the garden, and the air all round seemed to stir with scent, as if it were alive. He went across the bed of pinks, whose keen perfume came sharply across the rocking, heavy scent of the lilies, and stood alongside the white barrier of flowers. They flagged all loose, as if they were panting. The scent made him drunk. He went down to the field to watch the moon sink under.

A corncrake in the hay-close called insistently. The moon slid quite quickly downwards, growing more flushed. Behind him the great flowers leaned as if they were calling. And then, like a shock, he caught another perfume, something raw and coarse. Hunting round, he found the purple iris, touched their fleshy throats and their dark, grasping hands. At any rate, he had found something. They stood stiff in the darkness. Their scent was brutal. The moon was melting down upon the crest of the hill. It was gone; all was dark. The corncrake called still.

Breaking off a pink, he suddenly went indoors.

* * *

The Morels lived in a house in an ugly street that ran down a steep hill. The street itself was hideous. The house was rather superior to most. It was old, grimy, with a big bay window, and it was semi-detached; but it looked gloomy. Then Paul opened the door to the garden, and all was different. The sunny afternoon was there, like another land. By the path grew tansy and little trees. In front of the window was a plot of sunny grass, with old lilacs round it. And away went the garden, with heaps of dishevelled chrysanthemums in the sunshine, down to the sycamore-tree, and the field, and beyond one looked over a few red-roofed cottages to the hills with all the glow of the autumn afternoon.

* * *

He loved the Lincolnshire coast, and she loved the sea. In the early morning they often went out together to bathe. The grey of the dawn, the far, desolate reaches of the fenland smitten with winter, the sea-meadows rank with herbage, were stark enough to rejoice his soul. As they stepped on to the high-road from their plank bridge, and looked round at the endless monotony of levels, the land a little darker than the sky, the sea sounding small beyond the sandhills, his heart filled strong with the sweeping relentlessness of life. She loved him then. He was solitary and strong, and his eyes had a beautiful light.

They shuddered with cold; then he raced her down the road

to the green turf bridge. She could run well. Her colour soon came, her throat was bare, her eyes shone. He loved her for being so luxuriously heavy, and yet so quick. Himself was light; she went with a beautiful rush. They grew warm, and walked hand in hand.

A flush came into the sky, the wan moon, half-way down the west, sank into insignificance. On the shadowy land things began to take life, plants with great leaves became distinct. They came through a pass in the big, cold sandhills on to the beach. The long waste of foreshore lay moaning under the dawn and the sea; the ocean was a flat dark strip with a white edge. Over the gloomy sea the sky grew red. Quickly the fire spread among the clouds and scattered them. Crimson burned to orange, orange to dull gold, and in a golden glitter the sun came up, dribbling fierily over the waves in little splashes as if someone had gone along and the light had spilled from her pail as she walked.

The breakers ran down the shore in long, hoarse strokes. Tiny seagulls, like specks of spray, wheeled above the line of surf. Their crying seemed larger than they. Far away the coast reached out, and melted into the morning, the tussocky sandhills seeming to sink to a level with the beach. Mablethorpe was tiny on their right. They had alone the space of all this level shore, the sea, and the upcoming sun, the faint noise of the waters, the sharp crying of the gulls.

* * *

He shook hands and left her at the door of her cousin's house. When he turned away he felt the last hold for him had gone. The town, as he sat upon the car, stretched away over the bay of railway, a level fume of lights. Beyond the town the country, little smouldering spots for more towns—the sea—the night—on and on! And he had no place in it! Whatever spot he stood on, there he stood alone. From his breast, from his mouth, sprang the endless space, and it was there behind him, everywhere. The people hurrying along the streets offered no obstruction to the void in which he found himself. They were small shadows whose footsteps and voices could be heard, but in each of them the same night, the same silence. He got off the car. In the country all was dead still. Little stars shone high up; little stars spread far away in the flood-waters, a firmament below. Everywhere the vastness and terror of the immense night which is roused and stirred for a brief while by the day, but which returns, and will remain at last eternal, holding everything in its silence and its living gloom. There was no Time, only Space. Who could say his mother had lived and did not live? She had been in one place, and was in another; that was all. And his soul could not leave her, wherever she was. Now she was gone abroad into the night, and he was with her still. They were together. But yet there was his body, his chest, that leaned against the stile, his hands on the wooden bar. They seemed something. Where was he?—one tiny upright speck of flesh, less than an ear of wheat lost in the field. He could not bear it. On every side the immense dark silence seemed pressing him, so tiny a spark, into extinction, and yet, almost nothing, he could not be extinct. Night, in which everything was lost, went reaching out, beyond stars and sun. Stars and sun, a few bright grains, went spinning round for terror, and holding each other in embrace, there in a darkness that outpassed them all, and left them tiny and daunted. So much, and himself, infinitesimal, at the core a nothingness, and yet not nothing.

"Mother!" he whispered—"mother!"

She was the only thing that held him up, himself, amid all this. And she was gone, intermingled herself. He wanted her to touch him, have him alongside with her.

But no, he would not give in. Turning sharply, he walked towards the city's gold phosphorescence. His fists were shut, his mouth set fast. He would not take that direction, to the darkness, to follow her. He walked towards the faintly humming, glowing town, quickly.

From *THE PRUSSIAN OFFICER*

There was not the least difference between this morning and those of the bright springs, six or eight years back. White and sandy-gold fowls still scratched round the gate, littering the earth and the field with feathers and scratched-up rubbish. Between the two thick holly bushes in the wood-hedge was the hidden gap, whose fence one climbed to get into the wood; the bars were scored just the same by the keeper's boots. He was back in the eternal.

Syson was extraordinarily glad. Like an uneasy spirit he had returned to the country of his past, and he found it waiting for him, unaltered. The hazel still spread glad little hands downwards, the bluebells here were still wan and few, among the lush grass and in shade of the bushes.

The path through the wood, on the very brow of a slope, ran winding easily for a time. All around were twiggy oaks, just issuing their gold, and floor spaces diapered with woodruff, with patches of dog-mercury and tufts of hyacinth. Two fallen trees still lay across the track. Syson jolted down a steep, rough slope, and came again upon the open land, this time looking north as through a great window in the wood. He stayed to gaze over the level fields of the hill-top, at the village which strewed the bare upland as if it had tumbled off the passing wagons of industry, and been forsaken. There was a stiff, modern, grey little church, and blocks and rows of red dwellings lying at random; at the back, the twinkling headstocks of the pit, and the looming pit-hill. All was naked and out-of-doors, not a tree! It was quite unaltered.

* * *

He had come in full view of the downslope. The wide path ran from his feet like a river, and it was full of bluebells, save for a green winding thread down the centre, where the keeper walked. Like a stream the path opened into azure shallows at the levels, and there were pools of bluebells, with still the green thread winding through, like a thin current of ice-water through blue lakes. And from under the twig-purple of the bushes swam the shadowed blue, as if the flowers lay in flood water over the woodland.

"Ah, isn't it lovely!" Syson exclaimed; this was his past, the country he had abandoned, and it hurt him to see it so beautiful. Wood-pigeons cooed overhead, and the air was full of the brightness of birds singing.

* * *

Syson went round the buildings, and into the orchard at the back of the house, where daffodils all along the hedgerow swung like yellow, ruffled birds on their perches. He loved the place extraordinarily, the hills ranging round, with bear-skin woods covering their giant shoulders, and small red farms like brooches clasping their garments; the blue streak of water in the valley, the bareness of the home pasture, the sound of myriad-threaded bird-singing, which went mostly unheard. To his last day, he would dream of this place, when he felt the sun on his face, or saw the small handfuls of snow between the winter twigs, or smelt the coming of spring.

* * *

Instead of going straight to the highroad gate, Syson went along the wood's edge, where the brook spread out in a little bog, and under the alder trees, among the reeds, great yellow stools and bosses of marigolds shone. Threads of brown water trickled by, touched with gold from the flowers. Suddenly there was a blue flash in the air, as a kingfisher passed.

Syson was extraordinarily moved. He climbed the bank to the gorse bushes, whose sparks of blossom had not yet gathered into a flame. Lying on the dry brown turf, he discovered sprigs of tiny purple milkwort and pink spots of lousewort. What a wonderful world it was—marvellous, for ever new.

* * *

There was silence. The common, with its sere, blonde-headed thistles, its heaps of silent bramble, its brown-husked gorse in the glare of sunshine, seemed visionary. Across the brook began the immense pattern of agriculture, white checkering of barley stubble, brown squares of wheat, khaki patches of pasture, red stripes of fallow, with the woodland and the tiny village dark like ornaments, leading away to the distance, right to the hills, where the check-pattern grew smaller and smaller, till, in the blackish haze of heat, far off, only the tiny white squares of barley stubble showed distinct.

"Eh, I say, here's a rabbit hole!" cried Anne suddenly. "Should we watch if one comes out? You won't have to fidget, you know."

The two girls sat perfectly still. Frances watched certain objects in her surroundings: they had a peculiar, unfriendly look about them: the weight of greenish elderberries on their purpling stalks; the twinkling of the yellowing crab-apples that clustered high up in the hedge, against the sky: the exhausted, limp leaves of the primroses lying flat in the hedge-bottom: all looked strange to her. Then her eyes caught a movement. A mole was moving silently over the warm, red soil, nosing, shuffling hither and thither, flat, and dark as a shadow, shifting about, and as suddenly brisk, and as silent, like a very ghost of *joie de vivre*. Frances started, from habit was about to call on Anne to kill the little pest. But, to-day, her lethargy of unhappiness was too much for her. She watched the little brute paddling, snuffling, touching things to discover them, running in blindness, delighted to ecstasy by the sunlight and the hot, strange things that caressed its belly and its nose. She felt a keen pity for the little creature.

"Eh, our Fran, look there! It's a mole."

Anne was on her feet, standing watching the dark, unconscious beast. Frances frowned with anxiety.

"It doesn't run off, does it?" said the young girl softly. Then she stealthily approached the creature. The mole paddled fumblingly away. In an instant Anne put her foot upon it. not too heavily. Frances could see the struggling, swimming movement of the little pink hands of the brute, the twisting and twitching of its pointed nose, as it wrestled under the sole of the boot.

"It *does* wriggle!" said the bonny girl, knitting her brows in a frown at the eerie sensation. Then she bent down to look at her trap. Frances could now see, beyond the edge of the boot-sole, the heaving of the velvet shoulders, the pitiful turning of the sightless face, the frantic rowing of the flat, pink hands.

"Kill the thing," she said, turning away her face.

* * *

The house had a sterile appearance, as if it were still used, but not inhabited. A shadow seemed to go over her. She went across the lawn towards the garden, through an arch of crimson ramblers, a gate of colour. There beyond lay the soft blue sea within the bay, misty with morning, and the farthest headland of black rock jutting dimly out between blue and blue of the sky and water. Her face began to shine, transfigured with pain and joy. At her feet the garden fell steeply, all a confusion of flowers, and away below was the darkness of tree-tops covering the beck.

She turned to the garden that shone with sunny flowers around her. She knew the little corner where was the seat beneath the yew tree. Then there was the terrace where a great host of flowers shone, and from this, two paths went down, one at each side of the garden. She closed her sunshade and walked slowly among the many flowers. All round were rose-bushes, big banks of roses, then roses hanging and tumbling from pillars, or roses balanced on the standard bushes. By the open earth were many other flowers. If she lifted her head, the sea was upraised beyond, and the Cape.

Slowly she went down one path, lingering, like one who has gone back into the past. Suddenly she was touching some heavy crimson roses that were soft as velvet, touching them thoughtfully, without knowing, as a mother sometimes fondles the hand of her child. She leaned slightly forward to catch the scent. Then she wandered on in abstraction. Sometimes a flame-coloured, scentless rose would hold her arrested. She stood gazing at it as if she could not understand it. Again the same softness of intimacy came over her, as she stood before a tumbling heap of pink petals. Then she wondered over the white rose, that was greenish, like ice, in the centre. So, slowly, like a white, pathetic butterfly, she drifted down the path, coming at last to a tiny terrace all full of roses. They seemed to fill the place, a sunny, gay throng. She was shy of them, they were so many and so bright. They seemed to be conversing and laughing. She felt herself in a strange crowd. It exhilarated her, carried her out of herself. She flushed with excitement. The air was pure scent.

* * *

The small locomotive engine, Number 4, came clanking, stumbling down from Selston with seven full wagons. It appeared round the corner with loud threats of speed, but the colt that it startled from among the gorse, which still flickered indistinctly in the raw afternoon, out-distanced it at a canter. A woman, walking up the railway line to Underwood, drew back into the hedge, held her basket aside, and watched the foot-plate of the engine advancing. The trucks thumped heavily past, one by one, with slow inevitable movement, as she stood insignificantly trapped between the jolting black wagons and the hedge; then they curved away towards the coppice where the withered oak leaves dropped noiselessly, while the birds, pulling at the scarlet hips beside the track, made off into the dusk that had already crept into the spinney. In the open, the smoke from the engine sank and cleaved to the rough grass. The fields were dreary and forsaken, and in the marshy strip that led to the whimsey, a reedy pit-pond, the fowls had already abandoned their run among the alders, to roost in the tarred fowl-house. The pit-bank loomed up beyond the pond, flames like red sores licking its ashy sides, in the afternoon's stagnant light. Just beyond rose the tapering chimneys and the clumsy black headstocks of Brinsley Colliery. The two wheels were spinning fast up against the sky, and the winding-engine rapped out its little spasms. The miners were being turned up.

The engine whistled as it came into the wide bay of railway lines beside the colliery, where rows of trucks stood in harbour.

Miners, single, trailing and in groups, passed like shadows diverging home. At the edge of the ribbed level of sidings squat a low cottage, three steps down from the cinder track.

A large bony vine clutched at the house, as if to claw down the tiled roof. Round the bricked yard grew a few wintry primroses. Beyond, the long garden sloped down to a bush-covered brook course. There were some twiggy apple trees, winter-crack trees, and ragged cabbages. Beside the path hung dishevelled pink chrysanthemums, like pink cloths hung on bushes.

From *THE RAINBOW*

So the Brangwens came and went without fear of necessity, working hard because of the life that was in them, not for want of the money. Neither were they thriftless. They were aware of the last halfpenny, and instinct made them not waste the peeling of their apple, for it would help to feed the cattle. But heaven and earth was teeming around them, and how should this cease? They felt the rush of the sap in spring, they knew the wave which cannot halt, but every year throws forward the seed to begetting, and, falling back, leaves the young-born on the earth. They knew the intercourse between heaven and earth, sunshine drawn into the breast and bowels, the rain sucked up in the daytime, nakedness that comes under the wind in autumn, showing the birds' nests no longer worth hiding. Their life and interrelations were such; feeling the pulse and body of the soil, that opened to their furrow for the grain, and became smooth and supple after their ploughing, and clung to their feet with a weight that pulled like desire, lying hard and unresponsive when the crops were to be shorn away. The young corn waved and was silken, and the lustre slid along the limbs of the men who saw it. They took the udder of the cows, the cows yielded milk and pulse against the hands of the men, the pulse of the blood of the teats of the cows beat into the pulse of the hands of the men. They mounted their horses, and held life between the grip of their knees, they harnessed their horses at the wagon, and, with hand on the bridle-rings, drew the heaving of the horses after their will.

In autumn the partridges whirred up, birds in flocks blew like spray across the fallow, rooks appeared on the grey, watery heavens, and flew cawing into the winter. Then the men sat by the fire in the house where the women moved about with surety, and the limbs and the body of the men were impregnated with the day, cattle and earth and vegetation and the sky, the men sat by the fire and their brains were inert, as their blood flowed heavy with the accumulation from the living day.

The women were different. On them too was the drowse of blood-intimacy, calves sucking and hens running together in droves, and young geese palpitating in the hand while the food was pushed down their throttle. But the women looked out from the heated, blind intercourse of farm-life, to the spoken world beyond. They were aware of the lips and the mind of the world speaking and giving utterance, they heard the sound in the distance, and they strained to listen.

It was enough for the men, that the earth heaved and opened its furrow to them, that the wind blew to dry the wet wheat, and set the young ears of corn wheeling freshly round about; it was enough that they helped the cow in labour, or ferreted the rats from under the barn, or broke the back of a rabbit with a sharp knock of the hand. So much warmth and generating and pain and death did they know in their blood, earth and sky and beast and green plants, so much exchange and interchange they had with these, that they lived full and surcharged, their senses full fed, their faces always turned to the heat of the blood, staring into the sun, dazed with looking towards the source of generation, unable to turn round.

But the woman wanted another form of life than this, something that was not blood-intimacy. Her house faced out from the farm-buildings and fields, looked out to the road and the village with church and Hall and the world beyond. She stood to see the far-off world of cities and governments and the active scope of man, the magic land to her, where secrets were made known and desires fulfilled. She faced outwards to where men moved dominant and creative, having turned their back on the pulsing heat of creation, and with this behind them, were set out to discover what was beyond, to enlarge their own scope and range and freedom; whereas the Brangwen men faced inwards to the teeming life of creation, which poured unresolved into their veins.

* * *

There was green and silver and blue in the air about her now. And there was a strange insistence of light from the sea, to which she must attend. Primroses glimmered around, many of them, and she stooped to the disturbing influence near her feet, she even picked one or two flowers, faintly remembering in the new colour of life, what had been. All the day long, as she sat at the upper window, the light came off the sea, constantly, constantly, without refusal, till it seemed to bear her away, and the noise of the sea created a drowsiness in her, a relaxation like sleep. Her automatic consciousness gave way a little, she stumbled sometimes, she had a poignant, momentary vision of her living child, that hurt her unspeakably. Her soul roused to attention.

Very strange was the constant glitter of the sea unsheathed in heaven, very warm and sweet the graveyard, in a nook of the hill, catching the sunshine and holding it as one holds a bee between the palms of the hands, when it is benumbed. Grey grass and lichens and a little church, and snowdrops among coarse grass, and a cupful of incredibly warm sunshine.

She was troubled in spirit. Hearing the rushing of the beck away down under the trees, she was startled, and wondered what it was. Walking down, she found the bluebells around her glowing like a presence, among the trees.

Summer came, the moors were tangled with harebells like water in the ruts of the road, the heather came rosy under the skies, setting the whole world awake. And she was uneasy. She went past the gorse bushes shrinking from their presence, she stepped into the heather as into a quickening bath that almost hurt. Her fingers moved over the clasped fingers of the child, she heard the anxious voice of the baby, as it tried to make her talk, distraught.

And she shrank away again, back into her darkness, and for a long while remained blotted safely away from living. But autumn came with the faint red glimmer of robins singing, winter darkened the moors, and almost savagely she turned again to life, demanding her life back again, demanding that it should be as it had been when she was a girl, on the land at home, under the sky. Snow lay in great expanses, the telegraph posts strode over the white earth, away under the gloom of the sky. And savagely her desire rose in her again, demanding that this was Poland, her youth, that all was her own again.

* * *

Christmas passed, the wet, drenched, cold days of January recurred monotonously, with now and then a brilliance of blue flashing in, when Brangwen went out into a morning like crystal, when every sound rang again, and the birds were many and sudden and brusque in the hedges. Then an elation came over him in spite of everything, whether his wife were strange or sad, or whether he craved for her to be with him, it did not matter, the air rang with clear noises, the sky was like crystal, like a bell, and the earth was hard. Then he worked and was happy, his eyes shining, his cheeks flushed. And the zest of life was strong in him.

The birds pecked busily round him, the horses were fresh and ready, the bare branches of the trees flung themselves up like a man yawning, taut with energy the twigs radiated off into the clear light. He was alive and full of zest for it all. And if his wife were heavy, separated from him, extinguished, then, let her be, let him remain himself. Things would be as they would be. Meanwhile he heard the ringing crow of a cockerel in the distance, he saw the pale shell of the moon effaced on a blue sky.

So he shouted to the horses, and was happy.

* * *

" We'll just give the cows their something-to-eat, afore they go to bed," Brangwen was saying to her, holding her close and sure.

There was a trickling of water into the butt, a burst of raindrops sputtering on to her shawl, and the light of the lantern swinging, flashing on a wet pavement and the base of a wet wall. Otherwise it was black darkness : one breathed darkness.

He opened the doors, upper and lower, and they entered into the high, dry barn, that smelled warm even if it were not warm. He hung the lantern on the nail and shut the door. They were in another world now. The light shed softly on the timbered barn, on the white-washed walls and the great heap of hay; instruments cast their shadows largely, a ladder rose to the dark arch of a loft. Outside there was the driving rain, inside, the softly-illuminated stillness and calmness of the barn.

Holding the child on one arm, he set about preparing the food for the cows, filling a pan with chopped hay and brewer's grains and a little meal. The child, all wonder, watched what he did. A new being was created in her for the new conditions. Sometimes, a little spasm, eddying from the bygone storm of sobbing, shook her small body. Her eyes were wide and wondering, pathetic. She was silent, quite still.

In a sort of dream, his heart sunk to the bottom, leaving the surface of him still, quite still, he rose with the panful of food, carefully balancing the child on one arm, the pan in the other hand. The silky fringe of the shawl swayed softly, grains and hay trickled to the floor; he went along a dimly-lit passage behind the mangers, where the horns of the cows pricked out of the obscurity. The child shrank, he balanced stiffly, rested the pan on the manger wall, and tipped out the food, half to this cow, half to the next. There was a noise of chains running, as the cows lifted or dropped their heads sharply; then a contented, soothing sound, a long snuffing as the beasts ate in silence.

The journey had to be performed several times. There was the rhythmic sound of the shovel in the barn, then the man returned walking stiffly between the two weights, the face of the child peering out from the shawl. Then the next time, as he stopped, she freed her arm and put it round his neck, clinging soft and warm, making all easier.

The beasts fed, he dropped the pan and sat down on a box, to arrange the child.

"Will the cows go to sleep now?" she said, catching her breath as she spoke.

"Yes."

"Will they eat all their stuff up first?"

"Yes. Hark at them."

And the two sat still listening to the snuffing and breathing of cows feeding in the sheds communicating with this small barn. The lantern shed a soft, steady light from one wall. All outside was still in the rain. He looked down at the silky folds of the Paisley shawl. It reminded him of his mother. She used to go to church in it. He was back again in the old irresponsibility and security, a boy at home.

The two sat very quiet. His mind, in a sort of trance, seemed to become more and more vague. He held the child close to him. A quivering little shudder, re-echoing from her sobbing, went down her limbs. He held her closer. Gradually she relaxed, the eyelids began to sink over her dark, watchful eyes. As she sank to sleep, his mind became blank.

* * *

Corn harvest came on. One evening they walked out through the farm buildings at nightfall. A large gold moon hung heavily to the grey horizon, trees hovered tall, standing back in the dusk, waiting. Anna and the young man went on noiselessly by the hedge, along where the farm-carts had made dark ruts in the grass. They came through a gate into a wide open field where still much light seemed to spread against their faces. In the under-shadow the sheaves lay on the ground where the reapers had left them, many sheaves like bodies prostrate in shadowy bulk; others were riding hazily in shocks, like ships in the haze of moonlight and of dusk, farther off.

They did not want to turn back, yet whither were they to go, towards the moon? For they were separate, single.

"We will put up some sheaves," said Anna. So they could remain there in the broad, open place.

They went across the stubble to where the long rows of upreared shocks ended. Curiously populous that part of the field looked, where the shocks rode erect; the rest was open and prostrate.

The air was all hoary silver. She looked around her. Trees stood vaguely at their distance, as if waiting like heralds for the signal to approach. In this space of vague crystal her heart seemed like a bell ringing. She was afraid lest the sound should be heard.

"You take this row," she said to the youth, and passing on, she stooped in the next row of lying sheaves, grasping her hands in the tresses of the oats, lifting the heavy corn in either hand, carrying it, as it hung heavily against her, to the cleared space, where she set the two sheaves sharply down, bringing them together with a faint, keen clash. Her two bulks stood leaning together. He was coming, walking shadowily with the gossamer dusk, carrying his two sheaves. She waited near by. He set his sheaves with a keen, faint clash, next to her sheaves. They rode unsteadily. He tangled the tresses of corn. It hissed like a fountain. He looked up and laughed.

Then she turned away towards the moon, which seemed glowingly to uncover her bosom every time she faced it. He went to the vague emptiness of the field opposite, dutifully.

They stooped, grasped the wet, soft hair of the corn, lifted the heavy bundles, and returned. She was always first. She set down her sheaves, making a penthouse with those others. He was coming shadowy across the stubble, carrying his bundles. She turned away, hearing only the sharp hiss of his mingling corn. She walked between the moon and his shadowy figure.

She took her new two sheaves and walked towards him, as he rose from stooping over the earth. He was coming out of the near distance. She set down her sheaves to make a new stook. They were unsure. Her hands fluttered. Yet she broke away, and turned to the moon, which laid bare her bosom, so she felt as if her bosom were heaving and panting with moonlight. And he had to put up her two sheaves, which had fallen down. He worked in silence. The rhythm of the work carried him away again, as she was coming near.

They worked together, coming and going, in a rhythm which carried their feet and their bodies in tune. She stooped, she lifted the burden of sheaves, she turned her face to the dimness where he was, and went with her burden over the stubble. She hesitated, set down her sheaves, there was a swish and hiss of mingling oats, he was drawing near, and she must turn again. And there was the flaring moon laying bare her bosom again, making her drift and ebb like a wave.

He worked steadily, engrossed, threading backwards and forwards like a shuttle across the strip of cleared stubble, weaving the long line of riding shocks, nearer and nearer to the shadowy trees, threading his sheaves with hers.

And always, she was gone before he came. As he came, she drew away, as he drew away, she came. Were they never to meet? Gradually a low, deep-sounding will in him vibrated to her, tried to set her in accord, tried to bring her gradually to him, to a meeting, till they should be together, till they should meet as the sheaves that swished together.

And the work went on. The moon grew brighter, clearer, the corn glistened. He bent over the prostrate bundles, there was a hiss as the sheaves left the ground, a trailing of heavy bodies against him, a dazzle of moonlight on his eyes. And then he was setting the corn together at the stook. And she was coming near.

He waited for her, he fumbled at the stook. She came. But she stood back till he drew away. He saw her in shadow, a dark column, and spoke to her, and she answered. She saw the moonlight flash question on his face. But there was a space between them, and he went away, the work carried them, rhythmic.

Why was there always a space between them, why were they apart? Why, as she came up from under the moon, would she halt and stand off from him? Why was he held away from her? His will drummed persistently, darkly, it drowned everything else.

Into the rhythm of his work there came a pulse and a steadied purpose. He stooped, he lifted the weight, he heaved it towards her, setting it as in her, under the moonlit space. And he went back for more. Ever with increasing closeness he lifted the sheaves and swung striding to the centre with them, ever he drove her more nearly to the meeting, ever he did his share, and drew towards her, overtaking her. There was only the moving to and fro in the moonlight, engrossed, the swinging in the silence, that was marked only by the splash of sheaves, silence, and a splash of sheaves. And ever the splash of his sheaves broke swifter, beating up to hers, and ever the splash of her sheaves recurred monotonously, unchanging, and ever the splash of his sheaves beat nearer.

Till at last they met at the shock, facing each other, sheaves in hand. And he was silvery with moonlight, with a moonlit, shadowy face that frightened her.

* * *

But still it troubled Will Brangwen a little, in his orderly conventional mind, that the established rule of things had gone so utterly. One ought to get up in the morning and wash oneself and be a decent social being. Instead, the two of them stayed in bed till nightfall, and then got up, she never washed her face, but sat there talking to her father as bright and shameless as a daisy opened out of the dew. Or she got up at ten o'clock, and quite blithely went to bed again at three, or at half-past four, stripping him naked in the daylight, and all so gladly and perfectly, oblivious quite of his qualms. He let her do as she liked with him, and shone with strange pleasure. She was to dispose of him as she would. He was translated with gladness to be in her hands. And down went his qualms, his maxims, his rules, his smaller beliefs, she scattered them like an expert skittle-player. He was very much astonished and delighted to see them scatter.

He stood and gazed and grinned with wonder whilst his Tablets of Stone went bounding and bumping and splintering down the hill, dislodged for ever. Indeed, it was true as they said, that a man wasn't born before he was married. What a change indeed!

He surveyed the rind of the world: houses, factories, trams, the discarded rind; people scurrying about, work going on, all on the discarded surface. An earthquake had burst it all from inside. It was as if the surface of the world had been broken away entire: Ilkestone, streets, church, people, work, rule-of-the-day, all intact; and yet peeled away into unreality, leaving here exposed the inside, the reality: one's own being, strange feelings and passions and yearnings and beliefs and aspirations, suddenly become present, revealed, the permanent bedrock, knitted one rock with the woman one loved. It was confounding. Things are not what they seem! When he was a child, he had thought a woman was a woman merely by virtue of her skirts and petticoats. And now, lo, the whole world could be divested of its garment, the garment could lie there shed away intact, and one could stand in a new world, a new earth, naked in a new, naked universe. It was too astounding and miraculous.

This then was marriage! The old things didn't matter any more. One got up at four o'clock, and had broth at tea-time and made toffee in the middle of the night. One didn't put on one's clothes or one did put on one's clothes. He still was not quite sure it was not criminal. But it was a discovery to find one might be so supremely absolved. All that mattered was that he should love her and she should love him and they should live kindled to each other, like the Lord in two burning bushes that were not consumed. And so they lived for the time.

* * *

Then he turned to a book-shop and found a book on Bamberg Cathedral. Here was a discovery! here was something for him! He went into a quiet restaurant to look at his treasure. He lit up with thrills of bliss as he turned from picture to picture. He had found something at last, in these carvings. His soul had great satisfaction. Had he not come out to seek, and had he not found? He was in a passion of fulfilment. These were the finest carvings, statues, he had ever seen. The book lay in his hands like a doorway. The world around was only an enclosure, a room. But he was going away. He lingered over the lovely statues of women. A marvellous, finely-wrought universe crystallized out around him as he looked again, at the crowns, the twining hair, the woman-faces. He liked all the better the unintelligible text of the German. He preferred things he could not understand with the mind. He loved the undiscovered and the undiscoverable. He pored over the pictures intensely. And these were wooden statues, "Holz"—he believed that meant wood. Wooden statues so shapen to his soul! He was a million times gladdened. How undiscovered the world was, how it revealed itself to his soul. What a fine, exciting thing his life was, at his hand! Did not Bamberg Cathedral make the world his own? He celebrated his triumphant strength and life and verity, and embraced the vast riches he was inheriting.

* * *

Many days, she waited for the hour when he would be gone to work. Then the flow of her life, which he seemed to dam up, was let loose, and she was free. She was free, she was full of delight. Everything delighted her. She took up the rug and went to shake it in the garden. Patches of snow were on the fields, the air was light. She heard the ducks shouting on the pond, she saw them charge and sail across the water as if they were setting off on an invasion of the world. She watched the rough horses, one of which was clipped smooth on the belly, so that he wore a jacket and long stockings of brown fur, stand kissing each other in the wintry morning by the churchyard wall. Everything delighted her, now he was gone, the insulator, the obstruction removed, the world all hers, in connection with her.

She was joyfully active. Nothing pleased her more than to hang out the washing in a high wind that came full-butt over the round of the hill, tearing the wet garments out of her hands, making flap-flap-flap of the waving stuff. She laughed and struggled and grew angry. But she loved her solitary days.

* * *

Day after day came shining through the door of Paradise, day after day she entered into the brightness. The child in her shone till she herself was a beam of sunshine; and how lovely was the sunshine that loitered and wandered out of doors, where the catkins on the big hazel bushes at the end of the garden hung in their shaken, floating aureole, where little fumes like fire burst out from the black yew-trees as a bird settled clinging to the branches. One day bluebells were along the hedge-bottoms, then cowslips twinkled like manna, golden and evanescent on the meadows. She was full of a rich drowsiness and loneliness. How happy she was, how gorgeous it was to live: to have known herself, her husband, the passion of love and begetting; and to know that all this lived and waited and burned on around her, a terrible purifying fire, through which she had passed for once to come to this peace of golden radiance, when she was with child, and innocent, and in love with her husband and with all the many angels hand in hand. She lifted her throat to the breeze that came across the fields, and she felt it handling her like sisters fondling her, she drank it in perfume of cowslips and of apple blossoms.

* * *

Between east and west, between dawn and sunset, the church lay like a seed in silence, dark before germination, silenced after death. Containing birth and death, potential with all the noise and transitation of life, the cathedral remained hushed, a great, involved seed, whereof the flower would be radiant life inconceivable, but whose beginning and whose end were the circle of silence. Spanned round with the rainbow, the jewelled gloom folded music upon silence, light upon darkness, fecundity upon death, as a seed folds leaf upon leaf and silence upon the root and the flower, hushing up the secret of all between its parts, the death out of which it fell, the life into which it has dropped, the immortality it involves, and the death it will embrace again.

Here in the church, "before" and "after" were folded together, all was contained in oneness. Brangwen came to his consummation. Out of the doors of the womb he had come, putting aside the wings of the womb, and proceeding into the light. Through daylight and day-after-day he had come, knowledge after knowledge, and experience after experience, remembering the darkness of the womb, having prescience of the darkness after death. Then between-while he had pushed open the doors of the cathedral, and entered the twilight of both darknesses, the hush of the two-fold silence, where dawn was sunset, and the beginning and the end were one.

Here the stone leapt up from the plain of earth, leapt up in a manifold, clustered desire each time, up, away from the horizontal earth, through twilight and dusk and the whole range of desire, through the swerving, the declination, ah, to the ecstasy, the touch, to the meeting and the consummation, the clasp, the close embrace, the neutrality, the perfect, swooning consummation, the timeless ecstasy. There his soul remained, at the apex of the arch, clinched in the timeless ecstasy, consummated.

And there was no time nor life nor death, but only this, this timeless consummation, where the thrust from earth met the thrust from earth and the arch was locked on the keystone of ecstasy. This was all, this was everything. Till he came to himself in the world below. Then again he gathered himself together, in transit, every jet of him strained and leaped, leaped clear into the darkness above, to the fecundity and the unique mystery, to the touch, the clasp, the consummation, the climax of eternity, the apex of the arch.

* * *

Winter came, pine branches were torn down in the snow, the green pine needles looked rich upon the ground. There was the wonderful, starry, straight track of a pheasant's footsteps across the snow imprinted so clear; there was the lobbing mark of the rabbit, two holes abreast, two holes following behind; the hare shoved deeper shafts, slanting, and his two hind feet came down together and made one large pit; the cat podded little holes, and birds made a lacy pattern.

Gradually there gathered the feeling of expectation. Christmas was coming. In the shed, at nights, a secret candle was burning, a sound of veiled voices was heard. The boys were learning the old mystery play of St. George and Beelzebub. Twice a week, by lamplight, there was choir practice in the church, for the learning of old carols Brangwen wanted to hear. The girls went to these practices. Everywhere was a sense of mystery and rousedness. Everybody was preparing for something.

The time came near, the girls were decorating the church, with cold fingers binding holly and fir and yew about the pillars, till a new spirit was in the church, the stone broke out into dark, rich leaf, the arches put forth their buds, and cold flowers rose to blossom in the dim, mystic atmosphere. Ursula must weave mistletoe over the door, and over the screen, and hang a silver dove from a sprig of yew, till dusk came down, and the church was like a grove.

In the cow-shed the boys were blacking their faces for a dress-rehearsal; the turkey hung dead, with opened, speckled wings, in the dairy. The time was come to make pies, in readiness.

The expectation grew more tense. The star was risen into the sky, the songs, the carols were ready to hail it. The star was the sign in the sky. Earth too should give a sign. As evening drew on, hearts beat fast with anticipation, hands were full of ready gifts. There were the tremulously expectant words of the church service, the night was past and the morning was come, the gifts were given and received, joy and peace made a flapping of wings in each heart, there was a great burst of carols, the Peace of the World had dawned, strife had passed away, every hand was linked in hand, every heart was singing.

It was bitter, though, that Christmas Day, as it drew on to evening, and night became a sort of bank holiday, flat and stale. The morning was so wonderful, but in the afternoon and evening the ecstasy perished like a nipped thing, like a bud in a false spring. Alas, that Christmas was only a domestic feast, a feast of sweetmeats and toys! Why did not the grown-ups also change their everyday hearts, and give way to ecstasy? Where was the ecstasy?

How passionately the Brangwens craved for it, the ecstasy. The father was troubled, dark-faced and disconsolate, on Christmas night, because the passion was not there, because the day was become as every day, and hearts were not aflame. Upon the mother was a kind of absentness, as ever, as if she were exiled for all her life. Where was the fiery heart of joy, now the coming was fulfilled; where was the star, the Magi's transport, the thrill of new being that shook the earth?

* * *

At the end of supper, during dessert, the music began to play, violins, and flutes. Everybody's face was lit up. A glow of excitement prevailed. When the little speeches were over, and the port remained unreached for any more, those who wished were invited out to the open for coffee. The night was warm.

Bright stars were shining, the moon was not yet up. And under the stars burned two great, red, flameless fires, and round these lights and lanterns hung, the marquee stood open before a fire, with its lights inside.

The young people flocked out into the mysterious night. There was sound of laughter and voices, and a scent of coffee. The farm-buildings loomed dark in the background. Figures, pale and dark, flitted about, intermingling. The red fire glinted on a white or a silken skirt, the lanterns gleamed on the transient heads of the wedding guests.

To Ursula it was wonderful. She felt she was a new being. The darkness seemed to breathe like the sides of some great beast, the haystacks loomed half-revealed, a crowd of them, a dark, fecund lair just behind. Waves of delirious darkness ran through her soul. She wanted to let go. She wanted to reach and be amongst the flashing stars, she wanted to race with her feet and be beyond the confines of this earth. She was mad to be gone. It was as if a hound were straining on the leash, ready to hurl itself after a nameless quarry into the dark. And she was the quarry, and she was also the hound. The darkness was passionate and breathing with immense, unperceived heaving. It was waiting to receive her in her flight. And how could she start—and how could she let go? She must leap from the known into the unknown. Her feet and hands beat like a madness, her breast strained as if in bonds.

* * *

"The moon has risen," said Anton, as the music ceased, and they found themselves suddenly stranded, like bits of jetsam on a shore. She turned, and saw a great white moon looking at her over the hill. And her breast opened to it, she was cleaved like a transparent jewel to its light. She stood filled with the full moon, offering herself. Her two breasts opened to make way for it, her body opened wide like a quivering anemone, a soft, dilated invitation touched by the moon. She wanted the moon to fill in to her, she wanted more, more communion with the moon, consummation. But Skrebensky put his arm round her and led her away. He put a big, dark cloak round her, and sat holding her hand, whilst the moonlight streamed above the glowing fires.

She was not there. Patiently she sat, under the cloak, with Skrebensky holding her hand. But her naked self was away there beating upon the moonlight, dashing the moonlight with her breasts and her knees, in meeting, in communion. She half started, to go in actuality, to fling away her clothing and flee away, away from this dark confusion and chaos of people to the hill and the moon. But the people stood round her like stones, like magnetic stones, and she could not go, in actuality. Skrebensky like a loadstone weighed on her, the weight of his presence detained her. She felt the burden of him, the blind, persistent, inert burden. He was inert, and he weighed upon her. She sighed in pain. Oh, for the coolness and entire liberty and brightness of the moon. Oh, for the cold liberty to be herself, to do entirely as she liked. She wanted to get right away. She felt like bright metal weighted down by dark, impure magnetism. He was the dross, people were the dross. If she could but get away to the clean free moonlight.

* * *

He lived in a large new house of red brick, standing outside a mass of homogeneous red-brick dwellings, called Wiggiston. Wiggiston was only seven years old. It had been a hamlet of eleven houses on the edge of healthy, half-agricultural country. Then the great seam of coal had been opened. In a year Wiggiston appeared, a great mass of pinkish rows of thin, unreal dwellings of five rooms each. The streets were like visions of pure ugliness; a grey-black macadamized road, asphalt causeways, held in between a flat succession of wall, window, and door, a new-brick channel that began nowhere, and ended nowhere. Everything was amorphous, yet everything repeated itself endlessly. Only now and then, in one of the house-windows vegetables or small groceries were displayed for sale.

In the middle of the town was a large, open, shapeless space, or market-place, of black trodden earth, surrounded by the same flat material of dwellings, new red-brick becoming grimy, small oblong windows, and oblong doors, repeated endlessly, with just, at one corner, a great and gaudy public-house, and somewhere lost on one of the sides of the square, a large window opaque and darkish green, which was the post-office.

The place had the strange desolation of a ruin. Colliers hanging about in gangs and groups, or passing along the asphalt pavements heavily to work, seemed not like living people, but like spectres. The rigidity of the blank streets, the homogeneous amorphous sterility of the whole suggested death rather than life. There was no meeting place, no centre, no artery, no organic formation. There it lay, like the new foundations of a red-brick confusion rapidly spreading, like a skin-disease.

Just outside of this, on a little hill, was Tom Brangwen's big, red-brick house. It looked from the front upon the edge of the place, a meaningless squalor of ash-pits and closets and irregular rows of the backs of houses, each with its small activity made sordid by barren cohesion with the rest of the small activities. Farther off was the great colliery that went night and day. And all around was the country, green with two winding streams, ragged with gorse and heath, the darker woods in the distance.

The whole place was just unreal, just unreal. Even now, when he had been there for two years, Tom Brangwen did not believe in the actuality of the place. It was like some gruesome dream, some ugly, dead, amorphous mood become concrete.

* * *

She stood in the near end of the great room. There was a small high teacher's desk facing a squadron of long benches, two high windows in the wall opposite.

It was fascinating and horrible to Ursula. The curious, unliving light in the room changed her character. She thought it was the rainy morning. Then she looked up again, because of the horrid feeling of being shut in a rigid, inflexible air, away from all feeling of the ordinary day; and she noticed that the windows were of ribbed, suffused glass.

The prison was round her now! She looked at the walls, colour washed, pale green and chocolate, at the large windows with frowsy geraniums against the pale glass, at the long rows of desks, arranged in a squadron, and dread filled her. This was a new world, a new life, with which she was threatened. But still excited, she climbed into her chair at her teacher's desk. It was high, and her feet could not reach the ground, but must rest on the step. Lifted up there, off the ground, she was in office. How queer, how queer it all was! How different it was from the mist of rain blowing over Cossethay. As she thought of her own village, a spasm of yearning crossed her, it seemed so far off, so lost to her.

She was here in this hard stark reality—*reality*. It was queer, that she should call this the reality, which she had never known till to-day, and which now so filled her with dread and dislike, that she wished she might go away. This was the reality, and Cossethay, her beloved, beautiful, well-known Cossethay, which was as herself unto her, that was minor reality. This prison of a school was reality. Here, then, she would sit in state, the queen of scholars! Here she would realise her dream of being the beloved teacher bringing light and joy to her children! But the desks before her had an abstract angularity that bruised her sentiment and made her shrink. She winced, feeling she had been a fool in her anticipations. She had brought her feelings and her generosity to where neither generosity nor emotion were wanted. And already she felt rebuffed, troubled by the new atmosphere, out of place.

* * *

And she gave herself to all that she loved in Cossethay, passionately, because she was going away now. She wandered about to her favourite spots. There was a place where she went trespassing to find the snowdrops that grew wild. It was evening and the winter-darkened meadows were full of mystery. When she came to the woods an oak tree had been newly chopped down in the dell. Pale drops of flowers glimmered many under the hazels, and by the sharp, golden splinters of wood that were splashed about, the grey-green blades of snowdrop leaves pricked unheeding, the drooping, still little flowers were without heed.

Ursula picked some lovingly, in an ecstasy. The golden chips of wood shone yellow like sunlight, the snowdrops in the twilight were like the first stars of night. And she, alone amongst them, was wildly happy to have found her way into such a glimmering dusk, to the intimate little flowers, and the splash of wood chips like sunshine over the twilight of the ground. She sat down on the felled tree and remained awhile remote.

Going home, she left the purplish dark of the trees for the open lane, where the puddles shone long and jewel-like in the ruts, the land about her was darkened, and the sky a jewel overhead. Oh, how amazing it was to her! It was almost too much. She wanted to run, and sing, and cry out for very wildness and poignancy, but she could not run and sing and cry out in such a way as to cry out the deep things in her heart, so she was still, and almost sad with loneliness.

* * *

Term began. She went into town each day by train. The cloistered quiet of the college began to close around her.

She was not at first disappointed. The big college built of stone, standing in the quiet street, with a rim of grass and lime-trees all so peaceful: she felt it remote, a magic land. Its architecture was foolish, she knew from her father. Still, it was different from that of all other buildings. Its rather pretty, plaything, Gothic form was almost a style, in the dirty industrial town.

She liked the hall, with its big stone chimney-piece and its Gothic arches supporting the balcony above. To be sure the arches were ugly, the chimney-piece of cardboard-like carved stone, with its armorial decoration, looked silly just opposite the bicycle stand and the radiator, whilst the great notice-board with its fluttering papers seemed to slam away all sense of retreat and mystery from the far wall. Nevertheless, amorphous as it might be, there was in it a reminiscence of the wondrous, cloistral origin of education. Her soul flew straight back to the mediæval times, when the monks of God held the learning of men and imparted it within the shadow of religion. In this spirit she entered college.

The harshness and vulgarity of the lobbies and cloakrooms hurt her at first. Why was it not all beautiful? But she could not openly admit her criticism. She was on holy ground.

She wanted all the students to have a high, pure spirit, she wanted them to say only the real, genuine things, she wanted their faces to be still and luminous as the nuns' and the monks' faces.

Alas, the girls chattered and giggled and were nervous, they were dressed up and frizzed, the men looked mean and clownish.

Still, it was lovely to pass along the corridor with one's books in one's hands, to push the swinging, glass-panelled door, and enter the big room where the first lecture would be given. The windows were large and lofty, the myriad brown students' desks stood waiting, the great blackboard was smooth behind the rostrum.

Ursula sat beside her window, rather far back. Looking down, she saw the lime-trees turning yellow, the tradesman's boy passing silent down the still, autumn-sunny street. There was the world, remote, remote.

Here, within the great, whispering sea-shell, that whispered all the while with reminiscence of all the centuries, time faded away, and the echo of knowledge filled the timeless silence.

She listened, she scribbled her notes with joy, almost with ecstasy, never for a moment criticising what she heard. The lecturer was a mouth-piece, a priest. As he stood, black-gowned, on the rostrum, some strands of the whispering confusion of knowledge that filled the whole place seemed to be singled out and woven together by him, till they became a lecture.

At first, she preserved herself from criticism. She would not consider the professors as men, ordinary men who ate bacon, and pulled on their boots before coming to college. They were the black-gowned priests of knowledge, serving for ever in a remote, hushed temple. They were the initiated, and the beginning and the end of the mystery was in their keeping.

* * *

Often, they saw the pink of dawn away across the park. The tower of Westminster Cathedral was emerging, the lamps of Piccadilly, stringing away beside the trees of the park, were becoming pale and moth-like, the morning traffic was clock-clocking down the shadowy road, which had gleamed all night like metal, down below, running far ahead into the night, beneath the lamps, and which was now vague, as in a mist, because of the dawn.

Then, as the flush of dawn became stronger, they opened the glass doors and went out on to the giddy balcony, feeling triumphant as two angels in bliss, looking down at the still-sleeping world, which would wake to a dutiful, rumbling, sluggish turmoil of unreality.

* * *

He remained fairly easy, however, still in his state of heightened glamour, till she had gone, and he had turned away from St. Pancras, and sat on the tram-car going up Pimlico to the Angel, to Moorgate Street on Sunday evening.

Then the cold horror gradually soaked into him. He saw the horror of the City Road, he realized the ghastly cold sordidness of the tram-car in which he sat. Cold, stark, ashen sterility had him surrounded. Where then was the luminous, wonderful world he belonged to by rights? How did he come to be thrown on this refuse-heap where he was?

He was as if mad. The horror of the brick buildings, of the tram-car, of the ashen-grey people in the street made him reeling and blind as if drunk. He went mad. He had lived with her in a close, living, pulsing world, where everything pulsed with rich being. Now he found himself struggling amid an ashen-dry, cold world of rigidity, dead walls and mechanical traffic, and creeping, spectre-like people. The life was extinct, only ash moved and stirred or stood rigid, there was a horrible, clattering activity, a rattle like the falling of dry slag, cold and sterile. It was as if the sunshine that fell were unnatural light exposing the ash of the town, as if the lights at night were the sinister gleam of decomposition.

* * *

The dawn came. They stood together on a high place, an earthwork of the stone-age men, watching for the light. It came over the land. But the land was dark. She watched a pale rim on the sky, away against the darkened land. The darkness became bluer. A little wind was running in from the sea behind. It seemed to be running to the pale rift of the dawn. And she and he darkly, on an outpost of the darkness, stood watching for the dawn.

The light grew stronger, gushing up against the dark sapphire of the transparent night. The light grew stronger, whiter, then over it hovered a flush of rose. A flush of rose, and then yellow, pale, new-created yellow, the whole quivering and poising momentarily over the fountain on the sky's rim.

The rose hovered and quivered, burned, fused to flame, to a transient red, whilst the yellow urged out in great waves, thrown from the ever-increasing fountain, great waves of yellow flinging into the sky, scattering its spray over the darkness, which became bluer and bluer, paler, till soon it would itself be a radiance, which had been darkness.

The sun was coming. There was a quivering, a powerful, terrifying swim of molten light. Then the molten source itself surged forth, revealing itself. The sun was in the sky, too powerful to look at.

And the ground beneath lay so still, so peaceful. Only now and again a cock crew. Otherwise, from the distant yellow hills to the pine-trees at the foot of the Downs, everything was newly washed into being, in a flood of new, golden creation.

It was so unutterably still and perfect with promise, the golden-lighted, distinct land, that Ursula's soul rocked and wept. Suddenly he glanced at her. The tears were running over her cheeks, her mouth was working strangely.

"What is the matter?" he asked.

After a moment's struggle with her voice:

"It is so beautiful," she said, looking at the glowing, beautiful land. It was so beautiful, so perfect, and so unsullied.

He too realized what England would be in a few hours' time—a blind, sordid, strenuous activity, all for nothing, fuming with dirty smoke and running trains and groping in the bowels of the earth, all for nothing. A ghastliness came over him.

* * *

As she grew better, she sat to watch a new creation. As she sat at her window, she saw the people go by in the street below, colliers, women, children, walking each in the husk of an old fruition, but visible through the husk, the swelling and the heaving contour of the new germination. In the still, silenced forms of the colliers she saw a sort of suspense, a waiting in pain for the new liberation; she saw the same in the false, hard confidence of the women. The confidence of the women was brittle. It would break quickly to reveal the strength and patient effort of the new germination.

In everything she saw she grasped and groped to find the creation of the living God, instead of the old, hard barren form of bygone living. Sometimes great terror possessed her. Sometimes she lost touch, she lost her feeling, she could only know the old horror of the husk which bound in her and all mankind. They were all in prison, they were all going mad.

She saw the stiffened bodies of the colliers, which seemed already enclosed in a coffin, she saw their unchanging eyes, the eyes of those who are buried alive: she saw the hard, cutting edges of the new houses, which seemed to spread over the hill-side in their insentient triumph, the triumph of horrible, amorphous angles and straight lines, the expression of corruption triumphant and unopposed, corruption so pure that it is hard and brittle: she saw the dun atmosphere over the blackened hills opposite, the dark blotches of houses, slate-roofed and amorphous, the old church-tower standing up in hideous obsoleteness above raw new houses on the crest of the hill, the amorphous, brittle, hard-edged new houses advancing from

Beldover to meet the corrupt new houses from Lethley, the houses of Lethley advancing to mix with the houses of Hainor, a dry, brittle, terrible corruption spreading over the face of the land, and she was sick with a nausea so deep that she perished as she sat. And then, in the blowing clouds, she saw a band of faint iridescence colouring in faint colours a portion of the hill. And forgetting, startled, she looked for the hovering colour and saw a rainbow forming itself. In one place it gleamed fiercely, and, her heart anguished with hope, she sought the shadow of iris where the bow should be. Steadily the colour gathered, mysteriously, from nowhere, it took presence upon itself, there was a faint, vast rainbow. The arc bended and strengthened itself till it arched indomitable, making great architecture of light and colour and the space of heaven, its pedestals luminous in the corruption of new houses on the low hill, its arch the top of heaven.

And the rainbow stood on the earth. She knew that the sordid people who crept hard-scaled and separate on the face of the world's corruption were living still, that the rainbow was arched in their blood and would quiver to life in their spirit, that they would cast off their horny covering of disintegration, that new, clean, naked bodies would issue to a new germination, to a new growth, rising to the light and the wind and the clean rain of heaven. She saw in the rainbow the earth's new architecture, the old, brittle corruption of houses and factories swept away, the world built up in a living fabric of Truth, fitting to the over-arching heaven.

From *WOMEN IN LOVE*

She found herself, with the rest of the common women, drawn out on Friday evenings to the little market. Friday was pay-day for the colliers, and Friday night was market night. Every woman was abroad, every man was out, shopping with his wife or gathering with his pals. The pavements were dark for miles around with people coming in, the little market-place on the crown of the hill, and the main street of Beldover were black with thickly-crowded men and women.

It was dark, the market-place was hot with kerosene flares, which threw a ruddy light on the grave faces of the purchasing wives, and on the pale abstract faces of the men. The air was full of the sound of criers and of people talking, thick streams of people moved on the pavements towards the solid crowd of the market. The shops were blazing and packed with women, in the streets were men, mostly men, miners of all ages. Money was spent with almost lavish freedom.

The carts that came could not pass through. They had to wait, the driver calling and shouting, till the dense crowd would make way. Everywhere, young fellows from the outlying districts were making conversation with the girls, standing in the road and at the corners. The doors of the public-houses were open and full of light, men passed in and out in a continual stream, everywhere men were calling out to one another, or crossing to meet one another, or standing in little gangs and circles, discussing, endlessly discussing. The sense of talk, buzzing, jarring, half-secret, the endless mining and political wrangling, vibrated in the air like discordant machinery. And it was their voices which affected Gudrun almost to swooning. They aroused a strange, nostalgic ache of desire, something almost demoniacal, never to be fulfilled.

Like any other common girl of the district, Gudrun strolled up and down, up and down the length of the brilliant two-hundred paces of the pavement nearest the market-place. She knew it was a vulgar thing to do; her father and mother could not bear it; but the nostalgia came over her, she must be among the people. Sometimes she sat among the louts in the cinema: rakish-looking, unattractive louts they were. Yet she must be among them.

* * *

A young grey cat that had been sleeping on the sofa jumped

down and stretched, rising on its long legs, and arching its slim back. Then it sat considering for a moment, erect and kingly. And then, like a dart, it had shot out of the room, through the open window-doors, and into the garden.

"What's he after?" said Birkin, rising.

The young cat trotted lordly down the path, waving his tail. He was an ordinary tabby with white paws, a slender young gentleman. A crouching, fluffy, brownish-grey cat was stealing up the side of the fence. The Mino walked statelily up to her, with manly nonchalance. She crouched before him and pressed herself on the ground in humility, a fluffy soft outcast, looking up at him with wild eyes that were green and lovely as great jewels. He looked casually down on her. So she crept a few inches farther, proceeding on her way to the back door, crouching in a wonderful, soft, self-obliterating manner, and moving like a shadow.

He, going statelily on his slim legs, walked after her, then suddenly, for pure excess, he gave her a light cuff with his paw on the side of her face. She ran off a few steps, like a blown leaf along the ground, then crouched unobtrusively, in submissive, wild patience. The Mino pretended to take no notice of her. He blinked his eyes superbly at the landscape. In a minute she drew herself together and moved softly, a fleecy brown-grey shadow, a few paces forward. She began to quicken her pace, in a moment she would be gone like a dream, when the young grey lord sprang before her, and gave her a light, handsome cuff. She subsided at once, submissively.

"She is a wild cat," said Birkin. "She has come in from the woods."

The eyes of the stray cat flared round for a moment, like great green fires staring at Birkin. Then she had rushed in a soft swift rush half-way down the garden. There she paused to look round. The Mino turned his face in pure superiority to his master, and slowly closed his eyes, standing in statuesque young perfection. The wild cat's round, green, wondering eyes were staring all the while like uncanny fires. Then again, like a shadow, she slid towards the kitchen.

In a lovely springing leap, like a wind, the Mino was upon

her, and had boxed her twice, very definitely, with a white, delicate fist. She sank and slid back, unquestioning. He walked after her, and cuffed her once or twice, leisurely with sudden little blows of his magic white paws.

* * *

The lake was dim, the light dying from off it, in the midst of the dark land. The air all round was intangible, neither here nor there, and there was an unreal noise of banjoes, or suchlike music.

As the golden swim of light overhead died out, the moon gained brightness, and seemed to begin to smile forth her ascendancy. The dark woods on the opposite shore melted into universal shadow. And amid this universal undershadow, there was a scattered intrusion of lights. Far down the lake were fantastic pale strings of colour, like beads of wan fire, green and red and yellow. The music came out in a little puff, as the launch, all illuminated, veered into the great shadow, stirring her outlines of half-living lights, puffing out her music in little drifts.

All were lighting up. Here and there close against the faint water, and at the far end of the lake, where the water lay milky, in the last whiteness of the sky, and there was no shadow, solitary, frail flames of lanterns floated from the unseen boats. There was a sound of oars, and a boat passed from the pallor into the darkness under the wood, where her lanterns seemed to kindle into fire, hanging in ruddy lovely globes. And again, in the lake, shadowy red gleams hovered in reflection about the boat. Everywhere were these noiseless ruddy creatures of fire drifting near the surface of the water, caught at by the rarest, scarce visible reflections.

Birkin brought the lanterns from the bigger boat, and the four shadowy white figures gathered round, to light them. Ursula held up the first, Birkin lowered the light from the rosy, glowing cup of his hands, into the depths of the lantern. It was kindled, and they all stood back to look at the great blue moon of light that hung from Ursula's hand, casting a strange gleam on her face. It flickered, and Birkin went bending over the well of light. His face shone out like an apparition, so unconscious, and again, something demoniacal. Ursula was dim and veiled, looming over him.

* * *

To-morrow was Monday. Monday, the beginning of another school-week! Another shameful, barren school-week, mere routine and mechanical activity. Was not the adventure of death infinitely preferable? Was not death infinitely more lovely and noble than such a life? A life of barren routine, without inner meaning, without any real significance. How sordid life was, how it was a terrible shame to the soul, to live now! How much cleaner and more dignified to be dead! One could not bear any more of this shame of sordid routine and mechanical nullity. One might come to fruit in death. She had had enough. For where was life to be found? No flowers grow upon busy machinery, there is no sky to a routine, there is no space to a rotary motion. And all life was a rotary motion, mechanized, cut off from reality. There was nothing to look for from life—it was the same in all countries and all peoples. The only window was death. One could look out on to the great dark sky of death with elation, as one had looked out of the classroom window as a child, and seen perfect freedom in the outside. Now one was not a child, and one knew that the soul was a prisoner within this sordid vast edifice of life, and there was no escape, save in death.

But what a joy! What a gladness to think that whatever humanity did, it could not seize hold of the kingdom of death, to nullify that. The sea they turned into a murderous alley and a soiled road of commerce, disputed like the dirty land of a city every inch of it. The air they claimed too, shared it up, parcelled it out to certain owners, they trespassed in the air to fight for it. Everything was gone, walled in, with spikes on top of the walls, and one must ignominiously creep between the spiky walls through a labyrinth of life.

But the great dark, illimitable kingdom of death, there humanity was put to scorn. So much they could do upon earth, the multifarious little gods that they were. But the kingdom of death put them all to scorn, they dwindled into their true vulgar silliness in face of it.

How beautiful, how grand and perfect death was, how good to look forward to. There one would wash off all the lies and ignominy and dirt that had been put upon one here, a perfect bath of cleanness and glad refreshment, and go unknown, unquestioned, unabased. After all, one was rich, if only in the promise of perfect death. It was a gladness above all, that this remained to look forward to, the pure inhuman otherness of death.

Whatever life might be, it could not take away death, the inhuman transcendent death. Oh, let us ask no question of it, what it is or is not. To know is human, and in death we do not know, we are not human. And the joy of this compensates for all the bitterness of knowledge and the sordidness of our humanity. In death we shall not be human, and we shall not know. The promise of this is our heritage, we look forward like heirs to their majority.

From *LADY CHATTERLEY'S LOVER*

The car ploughed uphill through the long squalid straggle of Tevershall, the blackened brick dwellings, the black slate roofs glistening their sharp edges, the mud black with coal-dust, the pavements wet and black. It was as if dismalness had soaked through and through everything. The utter negation of natural beauty, the utter negation of the gladness of life, the utter absence of the instinct for shapely beauty which every bird and beast has, the utter death of the human intuitive faculty was appalling. The stacks of soap in the grocers' shops, the rhubarb and lemons in the greengrocers'! the awful hats in the milliners'! all went by ugly, ugly, ugly, followed by the plaster-and-gilt horror of the cinema with its wet picture announcements, " A Woman's Love ! ", and the new big Primitive chapel, primitive enough in its stark brick and big panes of greenish and raspberry glass in the windows. The Wesleyan chapel, higher up, was of blackened brick and stood behind iron railings and blackened shrubs. The Congregational chapel, which thought itself superior, was built of rusticated sandstone and had a steeple, but not a very high one. Just beyond were the new school buildings, expensive pink brick, and gravelled playground inside iron railings, all very imposing, and mixing the suggestion of a chapel and a prison. Standard Five girls were having a singing lesson, just finishing the la-me-do-la exercises and beginning a " sweet children's song." Anything more unlike song, spontaneous song, would be impossible to imagine : a strange bawling yell that followed the outlines of a tune. It was not like savages : savages have subtle rhythms. It was not like animals : animals *mean* something when they yell. It was like nothing on earth, and it was called singing. Connie sat and listened with her heart in her boots, as Field was filling petrol. What could possibly become of such a people, a people in whom the living intuitive faculty was dead as nails, and only queer mechanical yells and uncanny will-power remained ?

A coal-cart was coming down-hill, clanking in the rain. Field started upwards, past the big but weary-looking drapers' and clothing shops, the post-office, into the little market-place of forlorn space, where Sam Black was peering out of the door of the " Sun," that called itself an inn, not a pub, and where the commercial travellers stayed, and was bowing to Lady Chatterley's car.

The church was away to the left among black trees. The car slid on down-hill, past the " Miners' Arms." It had already passed the " Wellington," the " Nelson," the " Three Tuns " and the " Sun," now it passed the " Miners' Arms," then the Mechanics' Hall, then the new and almost gaudy Miners' Welfare and so, past a few new " villas," out into the blackened road between dark hedges and dark green fields, towards Stacks Gate.

Tevershall ! That was Tevershall ! Merrie England ! Shakespeare's England ! No, but the England of to-day, as Connie had realized since she had come to live in it. It was producing a new race of mankind, over-conscious on the money and social and political side, on the spontaneous, intuitive side dead,—but dead! Half-corpses, all of them: but with a terrible insistent consciousness in the other half. There was something uncanny and underground about it all. It was an underworld. And quite incalculable. How shall we understand the reactions in half-corpses? When Connie saw the great lorries full of steel-workers from Sheffield, weird, distorted, smallish beings like men, off for an excursion to Matlock, her bowels fainted and she thought: Ah, God, what has man done to man? What have the leaders of men been doing to their fellow-men? They have reduced them to less than humanness; and now there can be no fellowship any more! It is just a nightmare.

She felt again in a wave of terror the grey, gritty hopelessness of it all. With such creatures for the industrial masses, and the upper classes as she knew them, there was no hope, no hope any more. Yet he was wanting a baby, and an heir to Wragby! An heir to Wragby! She shuddered with dread.

Yet Mellors had come out of all this!—Yes, but he was as apart from it all as she was. Even in him there was no fellowship left. It was dead. The fellowship was dead. There was only apartness and hopelessness, as far as all this was concerned. And this was England, the vast bulk of England: as Connie knew, since she had motored from the centre of it.

The car was rising towards Stacks Gate. The rain was holding off, and in the air came a queer pellucid gleam of May. The country rolled away in long undulations, south towards the Peak, east towards Mansfield and Nottingham. Connie was travelling south.

As she rose on to the high country, she could see on her left, on a height above the rolling land the shadowy, powerful bulk of Warsop Castle, dark grey, with below it the reddish plastering of miners' dwellings, newish, and below those the plumes of dark smoke and white steam from the great colliery which put so many thousand pounds per annum into the pockets of the Duke and the other shareholders. The powerful old castle was a ruin, yet still it hung its bulk on the low sky-line, over the black plumes and the white that waved on the damp air below.

A turn, and they ran on the high level to Stacks Gate. Stacks Gate, as seen from the highroad, was just a huge and gorgeous new hotel, the "Coningsby Arms," standing red and white and gilt in barbarous isolation off the road. But if you looked, you saw on the left rows of handsome "modern" dwellings, set down like a game of dominoes, with spaces and gardens: a queer game of dominoes that some weird "masters" were playing on the surprised earth. And beyond these blocks of dwellings, at the back, rose all the astonishing and frightening overhead erections of a really modern mine, chemical works and long galleries, enormous, and of shapes not before known to man. The head-stocks and pit-bank of the mine itself were insignificant among the huge new installations. And in front of this, the game of dominoes stood for ever in a sort of surprise, waiting to be played.

This was Stacks Gate, new on the face of the earth since the war. But as a matter of fact, though even Connie did not know it, down-hill half a mile below the "hotel" was old Stacks Gate, with a little old colliery and blackish old brick dwellings, and a chapel or two and a shop or two and a little pub or two.

But that didn't count any more. The vast plumes of smoke and vapour rose from the new works up above, and this was now Stacks Gate: no chapels, no pubs, even no shops. Only the great "works," which are the modern Olympia with temples to all the gods: then the model dwellings: then the hotel. The hotel in actuality was nothing but a miners' pub, though it looked first-classy.

Even since Connie's arrival at Wragby this new place had arisen on the face of the earth, and the model dwellings had filled with riff-raff drifting in from anywhere, to poach Clifford's rabbits among other occupations.

The car ran on along the uplands, seeing the rolling county spread out. The county; it had once been a proud and lordly county. In front, looming again and hanging on the brow of the sky-line, was the huge and splendid bulk of Chadwick Hall, more window than wall, one of the most famous Elizabethan houses. Noble, it stood alone above a great park, but out of date, passed over. It was still kept up, but as a show place. "Look how our ancestors lorded it!"

That was the past. The present lay below. God alone knows where the future lies. The car was already turning, between little old blackened miners' cottages, to descend to Uthwaite. And Uthwaite, on a damp day, was sending up a whole array of smoke plumes and steam, to whatever gods there be. Uthwaite down in the valley, with all the steel threads of the railways to Sheffield drawn through it, and the coal-mines and the steel-works sending up smoke and glare from long tubes, and the pathetic little corkscrew spire of the church, that is going to tumble down, still pricking the fumes, always affected Connie strangely. It was an old market-town, centre of the dales. One of the chief inns was the "Chatterley Arms." There, in Uthwaite, Wragby was known as Wragby, as if it were a whole place, not just a house, as it was to outsiders: Wragby Hall, near Tevershall: Wragby, a "seat."

The miners' cottages, blackened, stood flush on the pavement, with that intimacy and smallness of colliers' dwellings over a hundred years old. They lined all the way. The road had become a street, and as you sank, you forgot instantly the open, rolling country where the castles and big houses still dominated, but like ghosts. Now you were just above the tangle of naked railway-lines, and foundries and other "works" rose about you, so big you were only aware of walls. And iron clanked with a huge reverberating clank, and huge lorries shook the earth, and whistles screamed.

Yet again, once you had got right down and into the twisted and crooked heart of the town, behind the church, you were in the world of two centuries ago, in the crooked streets where the "Chatterley Arms" stood, and the old pharmacy, streets which used to lead out to the wild open world of the castles and stately couchant houses.

But at the corner a policeman held up his hand as three lorries loaded with iron rolled past, shaking the poor old church. And not till the lorries were past could he salute her ladyship.

So it was. Upon the old crooked burgess streets hordes of oldish, blackened miners' dwellings crowded, lining the roads out. And immediately after these came the newer, pinker rows of rather larger houses, plastering the valley: the homes of more modern workmen. And beyond that again, in the wide rolling regions of the castles, smoke waved against steam, and patch after patch of raw reddish brick showed the newer mining settlements, sometimes in the hollows, sometimes gruesomely ugly along the sky-line of the slopes. And between, in between, were the tattered remnants of the old coaching and cottage England, even the England of Robin Hood, where the miners prowled with the dismalness of suppressed sporting instincts, when they were not at work.

England, my England! But which is *my* England. The stately homes of England make good photographs, and create the illusion of a connection with the Elizabethans. The handsome old halls are there, from the days of Good Queen Anne and Tom Jones. But smuts fall and blacken on the drab stucco, that has long ceased to be golden. And one by one, like the stately homes, they are abandoned. Now they are being pulled down. As for the cottages of England—there they are—great plasterings of brick dwellings on the hopeless countryside.

Now they are pulling down the stately homes, the Georgian halls are going. Fritchley, a perfect old Georgian mansion, was even now, as Connie passed in the car, being demolished. It was in perfect repair: till the war the Weatherleys had lived in style there. But now it was too big, too expensive, and the country had become too uncongenial. The gentry were departing to pleasanter places, where they could spend their money without having to see how it was made.

This is history. One England blots out another. The mines had made the halls wealthy. Now they were blotting them out, as they had already blotted out the cottages. The industrial England blots out the agricultural England. One meaning blots out another. The new England blots out the old England. And the continuity is not organic, but mechanical.

From *WOMEN IN LOVE*

THERE was a coffee-wagon on the platform. They drank hot, watery coffee, and ate the long rolls, split, with ham between, which were such a wide bite that it almost dislocated Ursula's jaw; and they walked beside the high trains. It was all so strange, so extremely desolate, like the underworld, grey, grey, dirt grey, desolate, forlorn, nowhere—grey, dreary nowhere.

At last they were moving through the night. In the darkness Ursula made out the flat fields, the wet flat dreary darkness of the Continent. They pulled up surprisingly soon—Bruges! Then on through the level darkness, with glimpses of sleeping farms and thin poplar trees and deserted high roads. She sat dismayed, hand in hand with Birkin. He, pale, immobile like a *revenant* himself, looked sometimes out of the window, sometimes closed his eyes. Then his eyes opened again, dark as the darkness outside.

A flash of a few lights on the darkness—Ghent station! A few more spectres moving outside on the platform—then the bell—then motion again through the level darkness. Ursula saw a man with a lantern come out of a farm by the railway, and cross to the dark farm-buildings. She thought of the Marsh the old, intimate farm-life at Cossethay. My God, how far was she projected from her childhood, how far was she still to go! In one lifetime one travelled through æons. The great chasm of memory from her childhood in the intimate country surroundings of Cossethay and the Marsh Farm—she remembered the servant Tilly, who used to give her bread and butter sprinkled with brown sugar, in the old living-room where the grandfather clock had two pink roses in a basket painted above the figures on the face—and now when she was travelling into the unknown with Birkin, an utter stranger—was so great, that it seemed she had no identity, that the child she had been, playing in Cossethay churchyard, was a little creature of history, not really herself.

They were at Brussels—half an hour for breakfast. They got down. On the great station clock it said six o'clock. They had coffee and rolls and honey in the vast deserted refreshment room, so dreary, always so dreary, dirty, so spacious, such desolation of space. But she washed her face and hands in hot water, and combed her hair—that was a blessing.

Soon they were in the train again and moving on. The greyness of dawn began. There were several people in the compartment, large florid Belgian business-men with long brown beards, talking incessantly in an ugly French she was too tired to follow.

It seemed the train ran by degrees out of the darkness into a faint light, then beat after beat into the day. Ah, how weary it was! Faintly, the trees showed, like shadows. Then a house, white, had a curious distinctness. How was it? Then she saw a village—there were always houses passing.

This was an old world she was still journeying through, winter-heavy and dreary. There was ploughland and pasture, and copses of bare trees, copses of bushes, and homesteads naked and work-bare. No new earth had come to pass.

She looked at Birkin's face. It was white and still and eternal, too eternal. She linked her fingers imploringly in his, under the cover of her rug. His fingers responded, his eyes looked back at her. How dark, like a night, his eyes were, like another world beyond! Oh, if he were the world as well, if only the world were he! If only he could call a world into being, that should be their own world!

The Belgians left, the train ran on, through Luxembourg, through Alsace-Lorraine, through Metz. But she was blind, she could see no more. Her soul did not look out.

They came at last to Basle, to the hotel. It was all a drifting trance, from which she never came to. They went out in the morning, before the train departed. She saw the street, the river, she stood on the bridge. But it all meant nothing. She remembered some shops—one full of pictures, one with orange velvet and ermine. But what did these signify ?—nothing.

She was not at ease till they were in the train again. Then she was relieved. So long as they were moving onwards, she was satisfied. They came to Zürich, then, before very long, ran under the mountains, that were deep in snow. At last she was drawing near. This was the other world now.

Innsbruck was wonderful, deep in snow, and evening. They drove in an open sledge over the snow : the train had been so hot and stifling. And the hotel, with the golden light glowing under the porch, seemed like a home.

From *THE LOST GIRL*

The train was very full. Next to Alvina sat a trim Frenchwoman reading *L'Aiglon*. There was a terrible encumbrance of packages and luggage everywhere. Opposite her sat Cicio, his black overcoat open over his pale-grey suit, his black hat a little over his left eye. He glanced at her from time to time, smiling constrainedly. She remained very still. They ran through Bromley and out into the open country. It was grey, with shivers of grey sunshine. On the downs there was thin snow. The air in the train was hot, heavy with the crowd and tense with excitement and uneasiness. The train seemed to rush ponderously, massively, across the Weald.

And so, through Folkestone to the sea. There was sun in the sky now, and white clouds, in the sort of hollow sky-dome above the grey earth with its horizon walls of fog. The air was still. The sea heaved with a sucking noise inside the dock.

Alvina and Cicio sat aft on the second-class deck, their bags near them. He put a white muffler round himself, Alvina hugged herself in her beaver scarf and muff. She looked tender and beautiful in her still vagueness, and Cicio, hovering about her, was beautiful too, his estrangement gave him a certain wistful nobility, which for the moment put him beyond all class inferiority. The passengers glanced at them across the magic of estrangement.

The sea was very still. The sun was fairly high in the open sky, where white cloud-tops showed against the pale, wintry blue. Across the sea came a silver sun-track. And Alvina and Cicio looked at the sun, which stood a little to the right of the ship's course.

"The sun!" said Cicio, nodding towards the orb and smiling to her.

"I love it," she said.

He smiled again, silently. He was strangely moved: she did not know why.

The wind was cold over the wintry sea, though the sun's beams were warm. They rose, walked round the cabins. Other ships were at sea—destroyers and battleships, grey, low, and sinister on the water. Then a tall bright schooner glimmered far down the channel. Some brown fishing-smacks kept together. All was very still in the wintry sunshine of the Channel.

So they turned to walk to the stern of the boat. And Alvina's heart suddenly contracted. She caught Cicio's arm, as the boat rolled gently. For there behind, behind all the sunshine, was England. England, beyond the water, rising with ash-grey, corpse-grey cliffs, and streaks of snow on the downs above. England like a long, ash-grey coffin slowly submerging. She watched it, fascinated and terrified. It seemed to repudiate the sunshine, to remain unilluminated, long and ash-grey and dead, with streaks of snow like cerements. That was England! Her thoughts flew to Woodhouse, the grey centre of it all. Home!

Her heart died within her. Never had she felt so utterly strange and far-off. Cicio at her side was as nothing, as spell-bound she watched, away off, behind all the sunshine and the sea, the grey, snow-streaked substance of England slowly receding and sinking, submerging. She felt she could not believe it. It was like looking at something else. What? It was like a long, ash-grey coffin, winter, slowly submerging in the sea. England?

From *THE LOST GIRL*

She was not in the village of Pescocalascio itself. That was a long hour's walk away. Pancrazio's house was the chief of a tiny hamlet of three houses, called Califano because the Califanos had made it. There was the ancient, savage hole of a house quite windowless, where Pancrazio and Cicio's mother had been born: the family home. Then there was Pancrazio's villa. And then, a little below, another newish, modern house in a sort of wild meadow, inhabited by the peasants who worked the land. Ten minutes' walk away was another cluster of seven or eight houses, where Giovanni lived. But there was no shop, no post nearer than Pescocalascio, an hour's heavy road up deep and rocky, wearying tracks.

And yet, what could be more lovely than the sunny days: pure, hot, blue days among the mountain foothills: irregular, steep little hills half wild with twiggy brown oak-trees and marshes and broom heaths, half cultivated, in a wild, scattered fashion. Lovely, in the lost hollows beyond a marsh, to see Cicio slowly ploughing with two great white oxen: lovely to go with Pancrazio down to the wild scrub that bordered the river-bed, then over the white-bouldered, massive desert and across stream to the other scrubby savage shore, and so up to the high road. Pancrazio was very happy if Alvina would accompany him. He liked it that she was not afraid. And her sense of the beauty of the place was an infinite relief to him.

Nothing could have been more marvellous than the winter twilight. Sometimes Alvina and Pancrazio were late returning with the ass. And then gingerly the ass would step down the steep banks, already beginning to freeze when the sun went down. And again and again he would balk the stream, while a violet-blue dusk descended on the white, wide stream-bed, and the scrub and lower hills became dark, and in heaven, oh, almost unbearably lovely, the snow of the near mountains was burning rose, against the dark-blue heavens. How unspeakably lovely it was, no one could ever tell, the grand, pagan twilight of the valleys, savage, cold, with a sense of ancient gods who knew the right for human sacrifice. It stole away the soul of Alvina. She felt transfigured in it, a clairvoyant in another mystery of life. A savage hardness came in her heart. The gods who had demanded human sacrifice were quite right, immutably right. The fierce, savage gods who dipped their lips in blood, these were the true gods.

* * *

Ah, the dreadful days of cold rain mingled with sleet, when the world outside was more than impossible, and the house inside was a horror. The natives kept themselves alive by going about constantly working, dumb and elemental. But what was Alvina to do?

For the house was unspeakable. The only two habitable rooms were the kitchen and Alvina's bedroom: and the kitchen, with its little grated windows high up in the wall, one of which had a broken pane and must keep one half of its shutters closed, was like a dark cavern vaulted and bitter with wood-smoke. Seated on the settle before the fire, the hard, greasy settle, Alvina could indeed keep the fire going, with faggots of green oak. But the smoke hurt her chest, she was not clean for one moment, and she could do nothing else. The bedroom again was just impossibly cold. And there was no other place. And from far away came the wild braying of an ass, primeval and desperate in the snow.

The house was quite large: but uninhabitable. Downstairs, on the left of the wide passage where the ass occasionally stood out of the weather, and where the chickens wandered in search of treasure, was a big, long apartment where Pancrazio kept implements and tools and potatoes and pumpkins, and where four or five rabbits hopped unexpectedly out of the shadows. Opposite this, on the right, was the cantina, a dark place with wine-barrels and more agricultural stores. This was the whole of the downstairs.

Going upstairs, half-way up, at the turn of the stairs was the opening of a sort of barn, a great wire-netting behind which showed a glow of orange maize-cobs and some wheat. Upstairs were four rooms. But Alvina's room alone was furnished. Pancrazio slept in the unfurnished room opposite, on a pile of old clothes. Beyond was a room with litter in it, a chest of drawers, and rubbish of old books and photographs Pancrazio had brought from England. There was a battered photograph of Lord Leighton, among others. The fourth room, approached through the corn-chamber, was always locked.

Outside was just as hopeless. There had been a little garden within the stone enclosure. But fowls, geese, and the ass had made an end of this. Fowl-droppings were everywhere, indoors and out, the ass left his pile of droppings to steam in the winter air on the threshold, while his heart-rending bray rent the air. Roads there were none: only deep tracks, like profound ruts with rocks in them, in the hollows, and rocky, grooved tracks over the brows. The hollow grooves were full of mud and water, and one struggled slipperily from rock to rock, or along narrow grass-ledges.

What was to be done, then, on mornings that were dark with sleet? Pancrazio would bring a kettle of hot water at about half-past eight. For had he not travelled Europe with English gentlemen, as a sort of model-valet! Had he not *loved* his English gentlemen? Even now, he was infinitely happier performing these little attentions for Alvina than attending to his wretched domains.

Cicio rose early, and went about in the haphazard, useless way of Italians all day long, getting nothing done. Alvina came out of the icy bedroom to the black kitchen. Pancrazio would be gallantly heating milk for her, at the end of a long stick. So she would sit on the settle and drink her coffee and milk, into which she dipped her dry bread. Then the day was before her.

She washed her cup and her enamelled plate, and she tried to clean the kitchen. But Pancrazio had on the fire a great black pot, dangling from the chain. He was boiling food for the eternal pig—the only creature for which any cooking was done. Cicio was tramping in with faggots. Pancrazio went in and out, back and forth from his pot.

Alvina stroked her brow and decided on a method. Once she was rid of Pancrazio, she would wash every cup and plate and utensil in boiling water. Well, at last Pancrazio went off with his great black pan, and she set to. But there were not six pieces of crockery in the house, and not more than six cooking utensils. These were soon scrubbed. Then she scrubbed the two little tables and the shelves. She lined the food-chest with clean paper. She washed the high window-ledges and the narrow mantelpiece, that had large mounds of dusty candle-wax in deposits. Then she tackled the settle. She scrubbed it also. Then she looked at the floor. And even she, English housewife as she was, realized the futility of trying to wash it. As well try to wash the earth itself outside. It was just a piece of stonelaid earth. She swept it as well as she could, and made a little order in the faggot-heap in the corner. Then she washed the little, high-up windows, to try and let in light.

And what was the difference? A dank wet soapy smell, and not much more. Maria had kept scuffling admiringly in and out, crying her wonderment and approval. She had most ostentatiously chased out an obtrusive hen, from this temple of cleanliness. And that was all.

It was hopeless. The same black walls, the same floor, the same cold from behind, the same green-oak wood-smoke, the same bucket of water from the well—the same come-and-go of aimless busy men, the same cackle of wet hens, the same hopeless nothingness.

Alvina stood up against it for a time. And then she caught a bad cold, and was wretched. Probably it was the wood-smoke.

But her chest was raw, she felt weak and miserable. She could not sit in her bedroom, for it was too cold. If she sat in the darkness of the kitchen she was hurt with smoke, and perpetually cold behind her neck. And Pancrazio rather resented the amount of faggots consumed for nothing. The only hope would have been in work. But there was nothing in that house to be done. How could she even sew?

She was to prepare the midday and evening meals. But with no pots, and over a smoking wood fire, what could she prepare? Black and greasy, she boiled potatoes and fried meat in lard, in a long-handled frying-pan. Then Pancrazio decreed that Maria should prepare macaroni with the tomato sauce, and thick vegetable soup, and sometimes polenta. This coarse, heavy food was wearying beyond words.

Alvina began to feel she would die, in the awful comfortless meaninglessness of it all. True, sunny days returned, and some magic. But she was weak and feverish with her cold, which would not get better. So that even in the sunshine the crude comfortlessness and inferior savagery of the place only repelled her.

* * *

It turned out quite a good job—a pleasant room with two windows, that would have all the sun in the afternoon, and would see the mountains on one hand, the far-off village perched up on the other. When she was well enough they set off one early Monday morning to the market in Ossona. They left the house by starlight, but dawn was coming by the time they reached the river. At the high road, Pancrazio harnessed the ass, and after endless delay they jogged off to Ossona. The dawning mountains were wonderful, dim-green and mauve and rose, the ground rang with frost. Along the roads many peasants were trooping to market, women in their best dresses, some of thick heavy silk with the white, full-sleeved bodices, dresses green, lavender, dark-red, with gay kerchiefs on the head: men muffled in cloaks, treading silently in their pointed skin sandals: asses with loads, carts full of peasants, a belated cow.

The market was lovely, there in the crown of the pass, in the old town, on the frosty sunny morning. Bulls, cows, sheep, pigs, goats stood and lay about under the bare little trees on the platform high over the valley: someone had kindled a great fire of brush-wood, and men crowded round, out of the blue frost. From laden asses vegetables were unloaded, from little carts all kinds of things, boots, pots, tin-ware, hats, sweet-things, and heaps of corn and beans and seeds. By eight o'clock in the December morning the market was in full swing: a great crowd of handsome mountain people, all peasants, nearly all in costume, with different head-dresses.

Cicio and Pancrazio and Alvina went quietly about. They bought pots and pans and vegetables and sweet-things and thick rush matting and two wooden armchairs and one old soft arm-chair, going quietly and bargaining modestly among the crowd, as Anglicized Italians do.

The sun came on to the market at about nine o'clock, and then from the terrace of the town gate Alvina looked down on the wonderful sight of all the coloured dresses of the peasant women, the black hats of the men, the heaps of goods, the squealing pigs, the pale lovely cattle, the many tethered asses —and she wondered if she would die before she became one with it altogether. It was impossible for her to become one with it altogether. Cicio would have to take her to England again, or to America. He was always hinting at America.

* * *

Suddenly, in the grey morning air, a wild music burst out: the drone of a bagpipe, and a man's high voice half singing, half yelling a brief verse, at the end of which a wild flourish on some other reedy wood instrument. Alvina sat still in surprise. It was a strange, high, rapid, yelling music, the very voice of the mountains. Beautiful, in our musical sense of the word, it was not. But oh, the magic, the nostalgia of the untamed, heathen past which it evoked.

"It is for Christmas," said Cicio. "They will come every day now."

Alvina rose and went round to the little balcony. Two men

stood below, amid the crumbling of finely falling snow. One, the elder, had a bagpipe whose bag was patched with shirting: the younger was dressed in greenish clothes, he had his face lifted, and was yelling the verses of the unintelligible Christmas ballad: short, rapid verses, followed by a brilliant flourish on a short wooden pipe he held ready in his hand. Alvina felt he was going to be out of breath. But no, rapid and high came the next verse, verse after verse, with the wild scream on the little new pipe in between, over the roar of the bagpipe. And the crumbs of snow were like a speckled veil, faintly drifting the atmosphere and powdering the littered threshold where they stood—a threshold littered with faggots, leaves, straw, fowls, and geese and ass droppings, and rag thrown out from the house, and pieces of paper.

The carol suddenly ended, the young man snatched off his hat to Alvina who stood above, and in the same breath he was gone, followed by the bagpipe. Alvina saw them dropping hurriedly down the incline between the twiggy wild oaks.

* * *

The village was wonderful. It occupied the crown of an eminence in the midst of the wide valley. From the terrace of the high road the valley spread below, with all its jumble of hills, and two rivers, set in the walls of the mountains, a wide space, but imprisoned. It glistened with snow under the blue sky. But the lowest hollows were brown. In the distance, Ossona hung at the edge of a platform. Many villages clung like pale swarms of birds to the far slopes, or perched on the hills beneath. It was a world within a world, a valley of many hills and townlets and streams shut in beyond access.

Pescocalascio itself was crowded. The roads were sloppy with snow. But none the less, peasants in full dress, their feet soaked in the skin sandals, were trooping in the sun, purchasing, selling, bargaining for cloth, talking all the time. In the shop, which was also a sort of inn, an ancient woman was making coffee over a charcoal brazier, while a crowd of peasants sat at the tables at the back, eating the food they had brought.

* * *

So the month of January passed, with its short days and its bits of snow and bursts of sunshine. On sunny days Alvina walked down to the desolate river-bed, which fascinated her. When Pancrazio was carrying up stone or lime on the ass, she accompanied him. And Pancrazio was always carrying up something, for he loved the extraneous jobs like building a fire-place much more than the heavy work of the land. Then she would find little tufts of wild narcissus among the rocks, gold-centred pale little things, many on one stem. And their scent was powerful and magical, like the sound of the men who came all those days and sang before Christmas. She loved them. There was green hellebore too, a fascinating plant—and one or two little treasures, the last of the rose-coloured Alpine cyclamens, near the earth, with snake-skin leaves, and so rose, so rose, like violets for shadowiness. She sat and cried over the first she found: heaven knows why.

In February, as the days opened, the first almond trees flowered among grey olives, in warm, level corners between the hills. But it was March before the real flowering began. And then she had continual bowlfuls of white and blue violets, she had sprays of almond blossom, silver-warm and lustrous, then sprays of peach and apricot, pink and fluttering. It was a great joy to wander looking for flowers. She came upon a bankside all wide with lavender crocuses. The sun was on them for the moment, and they were opened flat, great five-pointed, seven-pointed lilac stars, with burning centres, burning with a strange lavender flame, as she had seen some metal burn lilac-flamed in the laboratory of the hospital at Islington. All down the oak-dry bankside they burned their great exposed stars. And she felt like going down on her knees and bending her forehead to the earth in an oriental submission, they were so royal, so lovely, so supreme. She came again to them in the morning, when the sky was grey, and they were closed, sharp clubs, wonderfully fragile on their stems of sap, among leaves and old grass and wild periwinkle. They had wonderful dark stripes running up their cheeks, the crocuses, like the clear proud stripes on a badger's face, or on some proud cat. She took a handful of the sappy, shut, striped flames. In her room they opened into a grand bowl of lilac fire.

* * *

After a spell of hot, intensely dry weather she felt she would die in this valley, wither and go to powder as some exposed April roses withered and dried into dust against a hot wall. Then the cool wind came in a storm, the next day there was grey sky and soft air. The rose-coloured wild gladioli among the young green corn were a dream of beauty, the morning of the world. The lovely, pristine morning of the world, before our epoch began. Rose-red gladioli among corn, in among the rocks, and small irises, black-purple and yellow blotched with brown, like a wasp, standing low in little desert places, that would seem forlorn but for this weird, dark-lustrous magnificence. Then there were the tiny irises, only one finger tall, growing in dry places, frail as crocuses, and much tinier, and blue, blue as the eye of the morning heaven, which was a morning earlier, more pristine than ours. The lovely translucent pale irises, tiny and morning-blue, they lasted only a few hours. But nothing could be more exquisite, like gods on earth. It was the flowers that brought back to Alvina the passionate nostalgia for the place. The human influence was a bit horrible to her. But the flowers that came out and uttered the earth in magical expression, they cast a spell on her, bewitched her and stole her own soul away from her.

From *AARON'S ROD*

His hotel was not far from the cathedral square. Passing through the arcade, he came in sight of the famous cathedral with its numerous spines pricking into the afternoon air. He was not as impressed as he should have been. And yet there was something in the northern city—this big square with all the trams threading through, the little yellow Continental trams: and the spiny bulk of the great cathedral, like a grey-purple sea-urchin with many spines, on the one side, the ornamental grass-plots and flower-beds on the other: the big shops going all along the further strands, all round: and the endless, restless, nervous drift of a north Italian crowd, so nervous, so twitchy; nervous and twitchy as the slipping past of the little yellow tram-cars; it all affected him with a sense of strangeness, nervousness, and approaching winter. It struck him the people were afraid of themselves: afraid of their own souls, and that which was in their own souls.

Turning up the broad steps of the cathedral, he entered the famous building. The sky had cleared, and the freshened light shone coloured in living tablets round the wonderful, towering, rose-hearted dusk of the great church. At some altars lights flickered uneasily. At some unseen side-altar mass was going on, and a strange ragged music fluttered out on the incense-dusk of the great and lofty interior, which was all shadow, all shadow hung round with jewel tablets of light. Particularly beautiful the great east bay, above the great altar. And all the time, over the big-patterned marble floor, the faint click and rustle of feet coming and going, coming and going, like shallow, uneasy water rustled back and forth in a trough. A white dog trotted pale through the under-dusk, over the pale, big-patterned floor. Aaron came to the side altar where mass was going on, candles ruddily wavering. There was a small cluster of kneeling women—a ragged handful of onlooking men—and people wandering up and wandering away, young women with neatly dressed black hair, and shawls, but without hats; fine young women in very high heels; young men with nothing to do; ragged men with nothing to do. All strayed faintly clicking over the slabbed floor, and glanced at the flickering altar where the white-surpliced boys were curtseying and the white-and-gold priest was bowing, his hands over his breast, in the candle-light. All strayed, glanced, lingered, and strayed away again, as if the spectacle were not sufficiently holding. The bell chimed for the elevation of the Host. But the thin trickle of people trickled the same, uneasily, over the slabbed floor of the vastly-upreaching, shadow-foliaged cathedral.

* * *

Almost every shop had a flag flying. And every one of these flags now began to disappear, quickly or slowly, sooner or later, in obedience to the command of the vicious, derisive crowd, that marched and clotted slowly down the street, having its own way.

Only one flag remained flying: the big tri-colour that floated from the top storey of the house opposite Aaron's hotel. The ground floor of this house consisted of shop-premises—now closed. There was no sign of any occupant. The flag floated inert aloft.

The whole crowd had come to a stop immediately below the hotel, and all were now looking up at the green and white and red tri-colour which stirred damply in the early evening light, from under the broad eaves of the house opposite. Aaron looked at the long flag which drooped almost unmoved from the eaves-shadow, and he half expected it to furl itself up of its own accord, in obedience to the will of the masses. Then he looked down at the packed black shoulders of the mob below, and at the curious clustering pattern of a sea of black hats. He could hardly see anything but hats and shoulders, uneasily moving like boiling pitch away beneath him. But the shouts began to come up hotter and hotter. There had been a great banging of the shop door and a ringing of the bell of the guilty house door. The crowd—the swollen head of the procession—talked and shouted, occupying the centre of the street but leaving the pavement clear. A woman in a white blouse appeared in the shop-door. She came out and looked up at the flag and shook her head and gesticulated with her hands. It was evidently not her flag: she had nothing to do with it. The leaders now turned again to the large house-door, and began to ring all the bells and to beat with their fists. But no good—there was no answer. Voices arose, ragged and ironical. The woman explained again, with rapid gestures. Apparently there was nobody at home in the upper apartments—all entrances were locked—there was no caretaker to be found. Nobody owned the flag. There it hung under the broad eaves of the strong stone house, and didn't even know it was guilty. The woman went back into her shop and drew down the iron shutter from inside.

The crowd, nonplussed, now began to argue and shout and whistle. The voices rose in pitch and derision. Steam was getting up. There hung the gaudy flag. The mob crowded forward and filled the street in a mass below. All the rest of the street was empty and shut up. And still hung the showy rag, red and white and green, up aloft.

Suddenly there was a lull—then shouts, half-encouraging, half-derisive. And Aaron saw a smallish black figure of a youth, fair-haired, not more than seventeen years old, clinging like a monkey to the front of the house, and by the help of the heavy drain-pipe and the stone-work ornamentation climbing up to the stone ledge that ran beneath the ground-floor windows, up like a sudden cat on to the projecting footing. There he did not stop, but continued his race like some frantic lizard running up the great wall-front, working his way from the noise below as if in a frenzy of fright. It was one unending wriggling movement, sheer up the front of the impassive, heavy stone house.

The flag hung from a pole under one of the windows of the top storey—the third floor. Up went the wriggling figure of the possessed youth. The cries of the crowd below were now wild, ragged ejaculations of excitement and encouragement. The youth seemed to be lifted up, almost magically, on the intense upreaching excitement of the massed men below. He had passed the ledge of the first floor, like a lizard he wriggled up and passed the ledge or coping of the second floor, and there he was, like an upward-climbing shadow, scrambling on to the coping of the third floor. The crowd was for a second electrically still as the boy rose there erect, cleaving to the wall with the tips of his fingers.

But he did not hesitate for one breath. He was on his feet and running along the narrow coping that went across the house-front under the third-floor windows, running there on that narrow footing away above the street, straight to the flag. He had got it: he had clutched it on one hand, a handful of it. Exactly like a great flame rose the simultaneous yell of the crowd as the boy jerked and got the flag loose. He had torn it down, it was in his hand. A tremendous long yell, touched with a snarl of triumph, and searing like a puff of flame sounded as the boy remained for one moment with the flag in his fist looking down at the crowd below. His face was cold and elated and still. Then with the slightest gesture he threw the flag from him, and Aaron watched the gaudy remnant falling towards the many faces, whilst the noise of yelling rose up unheeded.

There was a great clutch and hiss in the crowd. The boy still stood unmoved, holding by one hand behind him, looking down from above, from his dangerous elevation, in a sort of abstraction.

And the next thing Aaron was conscious of was the sound of trumpets. A sudden startling challenge of trumpets, and out of nowhere a sudden rush of grey-green Carabinieri battering the crowd wildly with truncheons. It was so sudden that Aaron *heard* nothing any more. He only saw.

In utmost amazement he saw the sturdy, greeny-grey Carabinieri, like a posse of foot-soldiers, rushing thick and wild and indiscriminate on the crowd with a frenzied excitement which must have been based on fear: a sudden, new, excited crowd in uniform attacking the civilian crowd and laying about blindly, furiously, with truncheons. There was a seething moment in the street below. And almost instantaneously the original crowd burst into it in a frenzy of panic. A few black-hatted men fought furiously to get themselves free of the hated soldiers; in the confusion bunches of men staggered, reeled, fell, and were struggling among the legs of their comrades and of the Carabinieri. But the bulk of the crowd just burst and fled, in every direction. Like drops of water they seemed to fly up at the very walls themselves. They darted into any entry, any doorway. They sprang up the walls and clambered into the ground-floor windows. They sprang up the walls on to window ledges, and then jumped down again and ran: clambering, wriggling, darting, running in every direction; some cut, blood on their faces, terror or frenzy of flight in their hearts. Not so much terror as the frenzy of running away. In a breath the street was empty.

And all the time there above on the stone coping stood the long-faced, fair-haired boy, while four stout Carabinieri in the street below stood with uplifted revolvers and covered him, shouting that if he moved they would shoot. So there he stood, still looking down, still holding with his left hand behind him, covered by four revolvers. He was not so much afraid as twitchily self-conscious because of his false position.

Meanwhile down below the crowd had disappeared—melted momentaneously. The Carabinieri were busy arresting the men who had fallen and had been trodden underfoot, or who had let themselves foolishly be taken. Perhaps half a dozen men: half a dozen prisoners: less rather than more.

The sergeant ordered these to be secured between soldiers. And last of all the youth up above, still covered by the revolvers, was ordered to come down. He turned quite quietly, and quite humbly, cautiously picked his way along the coping to the drain-pipe. He reached this pipe and began in cautious dejection to climb down. It was a real climb down.

Once in the street he was seized by the grey uniforms. The soldiers formed up. The sergeant gave the order. And away marched authority, triumphant and thankful to have got off so lightly. The dejected youth was marched away between them.

* * *

It was a lovely day, a lovely, lovely day of early autumn. Over the great plain of Lombardy a magnificent blue sky glowed like midsummer, the sun shone strong. The great plain, with its great stripes of cultivation—without hedges or boundaries—how beautiful it was! Sometimes he saw oxen ploughing. Sometimes, oh so beautiful teams of eight, of ten, even of twelve pale, great soft oxen in procession, ploughing the dark velvety earth, a driver with a great whip at their head, a man far behind holding the plough-shafts. Beautiful the soft, soft plunging motion of oxen moving forwards. Beautiful the strange, snaky lifting of the muzzles, the swaying of the sharp horns. And the soft, soft crawling motion of a team of oxen, so invisible, almost, yet so inevitable. Now and again straight canals of water flashed blue. Now and again the great lines of grey-silvery poplars rose and made avenues or lovely grey airy quadrangles across the plain. Their top boughs were spangled with gold and green leaf. Sometimes the vine-leaves were gold and red, a patterning. And the great square farm-homesteads, white, red-roofed, with their outbuildings, stood naked amid the lands, without screen or softening. There was something big and exposed about it all. No more the cosy English ambushed life: no longer the cosy littleness of the landscape. A bigness —and nothing to shelter the unshrinking spirit. It was all exposed, exposed to the sweep of plain, to the high strong sky, and to human gaze. A kind of boldness, an indifference. Aaron was impressed and fascinated. He looked with a new interest at the Italians in the carriage with him—for this same boldness and indifference and exposed gesture. And he found it in them too. And again it fascinated him. It seemed so much bigger, as if the walls of life had fallen. Nay, the walls of English life will have to fall.

* * *

In the morning it was still November, and the dawn came slowly. And through the open window was the sound of the river's rushing. But the traffic started before dawn, with a bang and a rattle of carts, and a bang and jingle of tram-cars over the not-distant bridge. Oh noisy Florence! At half-past seven Aaron rang for his coffee: and got it at a few minutes past eight. The signorina had told him to take his coffee in bed.

Rain was still falling. But towards nine o'clock it lifted, and he decided to go out. A wet, wet world. Carriages going by, with huge wet shiny umbrellas, black and with many points, erected to cover the driver and the tail of the horse and the box-seat. The hood of the carriage covered the fare. Clatter-clatter through the rain. Peasants with long wagons and slow oxen, and pale-green huge umbrellas erected for the driver to walk beneath. Men tripping along in cloaks, shawls, umbrellas, anything, quite unconcerned. A man loading gravel in the river-bed, in spite of the wet. And innumerable bells ringing: but innumerable bells. The great soft trembling of the cathedral bell felt in all the air.

Anyhow it was a new world. Aaron went along close to the tall thick houses, following his nose. And suddenly he caught sight of the long slim neck of the Palazzo Vecchio up above, in the air. And in another minute he was passing between massive buildings, out into the Piazza della Signoria. There he stood still and looked round him in real surprise, and real joy. The flat, empty square with its stone paving was all wet. The great buildings rose dark. The dark, sheer front of the Palazzo Vecchio went up like a cliff, to the battlements, and the slim tower soared dark and hawk-like, crested, high above. And at the foot of the cliff stood the great naked David, white and stripped in the wet, white against the dark, warm-dark cliff of the building—and near, the heavy naked men of Bandinelli.

The first thing he had seen, as he turned into the square, was the back of one of these Bandinelli statues: a great naked man of marble, with a heavy back and strong naked flanks over which the water was trickling. And then to come immediately upon the David, so much whiter, glistening skin-white in the wet, standing a little forward, and shrinking.

He may be ugly, too naturalistic, too big, and anything else you like. But the David in the Piazza della Signoria, there under the dark great Palace, in the position Michelangelo chose for him, there, standing forward stripped and exposed and eternally half-shrinking, half-wishing to expose himself, he is the genius of Florence. The adolescent, the white, self-conscious, physical adolescent: enormous, in keeping with the stark, grim, enormous palace, which is dark and bare as he is white and bare. And behind, the big, lumpy Bandinelli men are in keeping too. They may be ugly—but they are there in their place, and they have their own lumpy reality. And this morning in the rain, standing unbroken, with the water trickling down their flanks and along the inner side of their great thighs, they were real enough, representing the undaunted physical nature of the heavier Florentines.

Aaron looked and looked at the three great naked men.

David so much white, and standing forward, self-conscious: then at the great splendid front of the Palazzo Vecchio: and at the fountain splashing water upon its wet, wet figures; and the distant equestrian statue; and the stone-flagged space of the grim square. And he felt that here he was in one of the world's living centres, here, in the Piazza della Signoria. The sense of having arrived—of having reached a perfect centre of the human world: this he had.

And so, satisfied, he turned round to look at the bronze Perseus which rose just above him. Benvenuto Cellini's dark hero looked female, with his plump hips and his waist, female and rather insignificant: graceful, and rather vulgar. The clownish Bandinellis were somehow more to the point. Then all the statuary in the Loggia! But that is a mistake. It looks too much like the yard of a monumental mason.

The great, naked men in the rain, under the dark-grey November sky, in the dark, strong, inviolable square! The wonderful hawk-head of the old palace! The physical, self-conscious adolescent, Michelangelo's David, shrinking and exposing himself, with his white, slack limbs! Florence, passionate, fearless Florence had spoken herself out. Aaron was fascinated by the Piazza della Signoria. He never went into the town, nor returned from it to his lodging, without contriving to pass through the square. And he never passed through it without satisfaction.

* * *

Aaron and Lilly sat on Argyle's little loggia, high up under the eaves of the house, a sort of long attic-terrace just under the roof, where no one would have suspected it. It was level with the grey conical roof of the Baptistery. Here sat Aaron and Lilly in the afternoon, in the last of the lovely autumn sunshine. Below, the square was already cold in shadow, the pink and white and green Baptistery rose lantern-shaped as from some sea-shore, cool, cold and wan now the sun was gone. Black figures, innumerable black figures, curious because they were all on end, up on end—Aaron could not say why he expected them to be horizontal—little black figures up on end, like fishes that swim on their tails, wiggled endlessly across the piazza, little carriages on natural all-fours rattled tinnily across, the yellow little tram-cars like dogs slipped round the corner. The balcony was so high up, that the sound was ineffectual. The upper space, above the houses, was nearer than the under-currents of the noisy town. Sunlight, lovely full sunlight, lingered warm and still on the balcony. It caught the façade of the cathedral sideways, like the tips of a flower, and sideways lit up the stem of Giotto's tower, like a lily stem, or a long, lovely pale pink and white and green pistil of the lily of the cathedral. Florence, the flowery town. Firenze—Fiorenze—the flowery town: the red lilies. The Fiorentini, the flower-souled. Flowers with good roots in the mud and muck, as should be: and fearless blossoms in air, like the cathedral and the tower and the David.

"I love it," said Lilly. "I love this place. I love the cathedral and the tower. I love its pinkness and its paleness. The gothic souls find fault with it, and say it is gimcrack and tawdry and cheap. But I love it; it is delicate and rosy, and the dark stripes are as they should be, like the tiger marks on a pink lily. It's a lily, not a rose: a pinky white lily with dark tigery marks. And heavy too, in its own substance: earth-substance, risen from the earth into the air: and never forgetting the dark, black-fierce earth—I reckon here men for a moment were themselves, as a plant in flower is for the moment completely itself. Then it goes off. As Florence has gone off. No flowers now. But it *has* flowered. And I don't see why a race should be like an aloe tree, flower once and die. Why should it? Why not flower again? Why not?"

From the introduction to *MEMOIRS OF THE FOREIGN LEGION*

It was a sunny day. I looked down on the farm cluster and the brown fields and the sere oak woods of the hill-crown, and the rocks and bushes savagely bordering it round. Beyond, the mountains with their snow were blue-glistery with sunshine, and seemed quite near, but across a sort of gulf. All was still and sunny. And the poignant grip of the past, the grandiose, violent past of the Middle Ages, when blood was strong and unquenched and life was flamboyant with splendours and horrible miseries, took hold of me till I could hardly bear it. It was really agony to me to be in the monastery and to see the old farm and the bullocks slowly working in the fields below, and the black pigs rooting among weeds, and to see a monk sitting on a parapet in the sun, and an old, old man in skin sandals and white bunched, swathed legs come driving an ass slowly to the monastery gate, slowly, with all that lingering nonchalance and wildness of the Middle Ages, and yet to know that I was myself, child of the present. It was so strange from M——'s window to look down on the plain and see the white road going straight past a mountain that stood like a loaf of sugar, the river meandering in loops, and the railway with glistening lines making a long black swoop across the flat and into the hills. To see trains come steaming, with white smoke flying. To see the station like a little harbour where trucks like shipping stood anchored in rows in the black bay of railway. To see trains stop in the station and tiny people swarming like flies! To see all this from the monastery, where the Middle Ages live on in a sort of agony, like Tithonus, and cannot die, this was almost a violation to my soul, made almost a wound.

* * *

In early April I went with my wife to Syracuse for a few days: lovely, lovely days, with the purple anemones blowing in the Sicilian fields, and Adonis-blood red on the little ledges, and the corn rising strong and green in the magical, malarial places, and Etna flowing now to the northward, still with her crown of snow. The lovely, lovely journey from Catania to Syracuse, in spring, winding round the blueness of that sea, where the tall pink asphodel was dying, and the yellow asphodel like a lily showing her silk. Lovely, lovely Sicily, the dawn-place, Europe's dawn, with Odysseus pushing his ship out of the shadows into the blue. Whatever had died for me, Sicily had then not died: dawn-lovely Sicily, and the Ionian sea.

We came back, and the world was lovely: our own house above the almond trees, and the sea in the cove below. Calabria glimmering like a changing opal away to the left, across the blue, bright straits, and all the great blueness of the lovely dawn-sea in front, where the sun rose with a splendour like trumpets every morning, and me rejoicing like a madness in this dawn, day-dawn, life-dawn, the dawn which is Greece, which is me.

From *WOMEN IN LOVE*

THEY went on into a snow meadow. There they were overtaken by the sledge, that came tinkling through the silence. It was another mile before they came upon Gudrun and Gerald on the steep up-climb, beside the pink, half-buried shrine.

Then they passed into a gulley, where were walls of black rock and a river filled with snow, and a still blue sky above. Through a covered bridge they went, drumming roughly over the boards, crossing the snow-bed once more, then slowly up and up, the horses walking swiftly, the driver cracking his long whip as he walked beside, and calling his strange wild *hue-hue !*, the walls of rock passing slowly by, till they emerged again between slopes and masses of snow. Up and up, gradually they went, through the cold shadow-radiance of the afternoon, silenced by the imminence of the mountains, the luminous, dazing sides of snow that rose above them and fell away beneath.

They came forth at last in a little high table-land of snow, where stood the last peaks of snow like the heart petals of an open rose. In the midst of the last deserted valleys of heaven stood a lonely building with brown wooden walls and white heavy roof, deep and deserted in the waste of snow, like a dream. It stood like a rock that had rolled down from the last steep slopes, a rock that had taken the form of a house, and was now half-buried. It was unbelievable that one could live there uncrushed by all this terrible waste of whiteness and silence and clear, upper, ringing cold.

Yet the sledges ran up in fine style, people came to the door laughing and excited, the floor of the hostel rang hollow, the passage was wet with snow, it was a real, warm interior.

The new-comers tramped up the bare wooden stairs, following the serving woman. Gudrun and Gerald took the first bedroom. In a moment they found themselves alone in a bare, smallish, close-shut room that was all of golden-coloured wood, floor, walls, ceiling, door, all of the same warm gold panelling of oiled pine. There was a window opposite the door, but low down, because the roof sloped. Under the slope of the ceiling were the table with wash-hand bowl and jug, and across, another table with mirror. On either side the door were two beds piled high with an enormous blue-checked overbolster, enormous.

This was all—no cupboard, none of the amenities of life. Here they were shut up together in this cell of golden-coloured wood, with two blue-checked beds. They looked at each other and laughed, frightened by this naked nearness of isolation.

* * *

Suddenly she wanted to go away. It occurred to her, like a miracle, that she might go away into another world. She had felt so doomed up here in the eternal snow, as if there were no beyond.

Now suddenly, as by a miracle she remembered that away beyond, below her, lay the dark fruitful earth, that towards the south there were stretches of land dark with orange trees and cypress, grey with olives, that ilex trees lifted wonderful plumy tufts in shadow against a blue sky. Miracle of miracles !—this utterly silent, frozen world of the mountain-tops was not universal ! One might leave it and have done with it. One might go away.

She wanted to realize the miracle at once. She wanted at this instant to have done with the snow-world, the terrible, static ice-built mountain tops. She wanted to see the dark earth, to smell its earthy fecundity, to see the patient wintry vegetation, to feel the sunshine touch a response in the buds.

From *THE LADYBIRD*

The shops were all shut, but peasants from the hills were already strolling about, in their holiday dress: the men in their short leather trousers, like football drawers, and bare brown knees, and great boots: their little grey jackets faced with green, and their green hats with the proud chamois-brush behind. They seemed to stray about like lost souls, and the proud chamois-brush behind their hats, this proud, cocky, perking-up tail, like a mountain-buck with his tail up, was belied by the lost-soul look of the men, as they loitered about with their hands shoved in the front pockets of their trousers. Some women also were creeping about: peasant women, in the funny little black hats that had thick gold under the brim and long black streamers of ribbon, broad, black, water-wave ribbon starting from a bow under the brim behind, and streaming right to the bottom of the skirt. These women, in their thick, dark dresses, with tight bodices, and massive, heavy, full skirts, and bright or dark aprons, strode about with the heavy stride of the mountain women, the heavy, quick, forward-leaning motion. They were waiting for the town-day to begin.

Hepburn had a knapsack on his back, with food for the day. But bread was wanting. They found the door of the bakery open, and got a loaf: a long, hot loaf of pure white bread, beautiful sweet bread. It cost seventy kronen. To Hepburn it was always a mystery where this exquisite bread came from, in a lost land.

In the little square where the clock stood were bunches of people, and a big motor-omnibus, and a motor-car that would hold about eight people. Hepburn had paid his seven hundred kronen for the two tickets. Hannele tied up her head in a thin scarf, and put on her thick coat. She and Hepburn sat in front by the peaked driver. And at seven o'clock away went the car, swooping out of the town, past the handsome old Tyrolese Schloss, or manor, black-and-white, with its little black spires pricking up, past the station, and under the trees by the lake-side. The road was not good, but they ran at a great speed, out past the end of the lake, where the reeds grew, out into the open valley-mouth, where the mountains opened in two clefts. It was cold in the car. Hepburn buttoned himself up to the throat and pulled his hat down on his ears. Hannele's scarf fluttered. She sat without saying anything, erect, her face fine and keen, watching ahead. From the deep Pinzgau valley came the river roaring and raging, a glacier river of pale, seething ice-water. Over went the car, over the log bridge, darting towards the great slopes opposite. And then a sudden immense turn, a swerve under the height of the mountain side, and again a darting lurch forward, under the pear-trees of the high-road, past the big old ruined castle that so magnificently watched the valley mouth, and the foaming river; on, rushing under the huge roofs of the balconied peasant houses of a village, then swinging again to take another valley mouth, there where a little village clustered all black and white on a knoll, with a white church that had a black steeple, and a white castle with black spines, and clustering, ample black-and-white houses of the Tyrol. There is a grandeur even in the peasant houses, with their great wide passage halls where the swallows build, and where one could build a whole English cottage.

* * *

The grasses hanging on the rock face were still dewy. There were a few wild raspberries, and a tiny tuft of bilberries with blackberries here and there, and a few tufts of unripe cranberries. The many hundreds of tourists who passed up and down did not leave much to pick. Some mountain hare-bells, like bells of blue water, hung coldly glistening in their darkness. Sometimes the hairy mountain-bell, pale-blue and bristling, stood alone, curving his head right down, stiff and taut. There was an occasional big, moist, lolling daisy.

So the two climbed slowly up the steep ledge of a road. This valley was just a mountain cleft, cleft sheer in the hard, living rock, with black trees like hair flourishing in this secret, naked place of the earth. At the bottom of the open wedge for ever roared the rampant, insatiable water. The sky from above was like a sharp wedge forcing its way into the earth's cleavage, and that eternal ferocious water was like the steel edge of the wedge, the terrible tip biting in into the rocks' intensity. Who could have thought that the soft sky of light, and the soft foam of water could thrust and penetrate into the dark, strong earth? But so it was. Hannele and Hepburn, toiling up the steep little ledge of a road that hung half-way down the gulf, looked back, time after time, back down upon the brown timbers and shingle roofs of the hotel, that now, away below, looked damp and wedged in like boulders. Then back at the next tourists struggling up. Then down at the water, that rushed like a beast of prey. And then, as they rose higher, they looked up also, at the livid great sides of rock, livid bare rock that sloped from the sky-ridge in a hideous sheer swerve downwards.

* * *

So they trudged on round the bluff, and then in front of them saw what is always, always wonderful, one of those shallow upper valleys, naked, where the first waters are rocked. A flat, shallow, utterly desolate valley, wide as a wide bowl under the sky, with rock slopes and grey stone-slides and precipices all around, and the zig-zag of snow-stripes and ice-roots descending, and then rivers, streams and rivers rushing from many points downwards, down out of the ice-roots and the snow-dagger-points, waters rushing in newly-liberated frenzy downwards, down in waterfalls and cascades and threads, down into the wide, shallow bed of the valley, strewn with rocks and stones innumerable, and not a tree, not a visible bush.

Only, of course, two hotels or restaurant places. But these no more than low, sprawling, peasant-looking places lost among the stones, with stones on their roofs so that they seemed just a part of the valley bed. There was the valley, dotted with rock and rolled-down stone, and these two house-places, and woven with innumerable new waters, and one hoarse stone-tracked river in the desert, and the thin road-track winding along the desolate flat, past first one house, then the other, over one stream, then another, on to the far rock-face above which the glacier seemed to loll like some awful great tongue put out.

"Ah, it is wonderful!" he said, as if to himself.

And she looked quickly at his face, saw the queer, blank, sphinx-look with which he gazed out beyond himself. His eyes were black and set, and he seemed so motionless, as if he were eternal facing these upper facts.

She thrilled with triumph. She felt he was overcome.

"It *is* wonderful," she said.

"Wonderful. And for ever wonderful," he said.

"Ah, in *winter*——" she cried.

His face changed, and he looked at her.

"In winter you couldn't get up here," he said.

They went on. Up the slopes cattle were feeding: came that isolated tong-tong-tong of cowbells, dropping like the slow clink of ice on the arrested air. The sound always woke in him a primeval, almost hopeless melancholy. Always made him feel *navré*. He looked round. There was no tree, no bush, only great grey rocks and pale boulders scattered in place of trees and bushes. But yes, clinging on one side like a dark close beard were the alpenrose shrubs.

"In May," he said, "that side there must be all pink with alpenroses."

"I *must* come. I *must* come!" she cried.

There were tourists dotted along the road: and two tiny low carts drawn by silky, long-eared mules. These carts went right down to meet the motor-cars, and to bring up provisions for the Glacier Hotel: for there was still another big hotel ahead. Hepburn was happy in that upper valley, that first rocking cradle of early water. He liked to see the great fangs and slashes of ice and snow thrust down into the rock, as if the ice had bitten into the flesh of the earth. And from the fang-tips the hoarse water crying its birth-cry, rushing down.

By the turfy road and under the rocks were many flowers: wonderful hare-bells, big and cold and dark, almost black, and seeming like purple-dark ice: then little tufts of tiny pale-blue bells, as if some fairy frog had been blowing spume-bubbles out of the ice: then the bishop's-crosier of the stiff, bigger, hairy mountain-bell: then many stars of pale-lavender gentian, touched with earth-colour: and then monkshood, yellow, primrose yellow monkshood and sudden places full of dark monkshood. That dark-blue, black-blue, terrible colour of the strange rich monkshood made Hepburn look and look and look again. How did the ice come by that lustrous blue-purple intense darkness?—and by that royal poison?—that laughing-snake gorgeousness of much monkshood.

* * *

The rain had ceased. There was a wisp of sunshine from a grey sky. Alexander left the knapsack, and the two went out into the air. Before them lay the last level of the up-climb, the Lammerboden. It was a rather gruesome hollow between the peaks, a last shallow valley about a mile long. At the end the enormous static stream of the glacier poured in from the blunt mountain-top of ice. The ice was dull, sullen-coloured, melted on the surface by the very hot summer: and so it seemed a huge, arrested, sodden flood, ending in a wave-wall of stone-speckled ice upon the valley bed of rocky debris. A gruesome descent of stone and blocks of rock, the little valley bed, with a river raving through. On the left rose the grey rock, but the glacier was there, sending down great paws of ice. It was like some great deep-furred ice-bear lying spread upon the top heights, and reaching down terrible paws of ice into the valley: like some immense sky-bear fishing in the earth's solid hollows from above. Hepburn it just filled with terror. Hannele too it scared, but it gave her a sense of ecstasy. Some of the immense, furrowed paws of ice held down between the rock were vivid blue in colour, but of a frightening, poisonous blue, like crystal copper-sulphate. Most of the ice was a sullen, semi-translucent greeny grey.

The two set off to walk through the massy, desolate stone-bed, under rocks and over waters, to the main glacier. The flowers were even more beautiful on this last reach. Particularly the dark hare-bells were large and almost black and ice-metallic: one could imagine they gave a dull ice-chink. And the grass of Parnassus stood erect, white-veined big cups held terribly naked and open to their ice-air.

From behind the great blunt summit of ice that blocked the distance at the end of the valley, a pale-grey woolly mist or cloud was fusing up, exhaling huge, like some grey-dead aura into the sky and covering the top of the glacier. All the way along the valley people were threading, strangely insignificant, among the grey dishevel of stone and rock, like insects. Hannele and Alexander went ahead quickly, along the tiring track.

"Are you glad now that you came?" she said, looking at him triumphant.

"Very glad I came," he said. His eyes were dilated with excitement that was ordeal or mystic battle rather than the Bergheil ecstasy. The curious vibration of his excitement made the scene strange, rather horrible to her. She too shuddered. But it still seemed to her to hold the key to all glamour and ecstasy, the great silent, living glacier. It seemed to her like a grand beast.

As they came near they saw the wall of ice: the glacier end, thick crusted and speckled with stone and dirt debris. From underneath, secret in stones, water rushed out. When they came quite near, they saw the great monster was sweating all over, trickles and rivulets of sweat running down his sides of pure, slush-translucent ice. There it was, the glacier, ending abruptly in the wall of ice under which they stood. Near to, the ice was pure, but water-logged, all the surface rather rotten from the hot summer. It was sullenly translucent, and of a watery, darkish bluey-green colour. But near the earth it became again bright coloured, gleams of green like jade, gleams of blue like thin, pale sapphire, in little caverns above the wet stones where the walls trickled for ever.

From *THE WOMAN WHO RODE AWAY*

The wind blew icily in the street. The town seemed empty, as if its spirit had left it. The few squat, hefty foot-passengers were all talking the harsh Alsatian German. Shop-signs were in

French, often with a little concession to German underneath. And the shops were full of goods, glutted with goods from the once-German factories of Mulhausen and other cities.

She crossed the night-dark river, where the wash-houses of the washerwomen were anchored along the stream, a few odd women still kneeling over the water's edge, in the dim electric light, rinsing their clothes in the grim, cold water. In the big square the icy wind was blowing, and the place seemed a desert. A city once more conquered.

After all she could not remember her way to the cathedral. She saw a French policeman in his blue cape and peaked cap, looking a lonely, vulnerable, silky specimen in this harsh Alsatian city. Crossing over to him she asked him in French where was the cathedral.

He pointed out to her, the first turning on the left. He did not seem hostile; nobody seemed really hostile. Only the great frozen weariness of winter in a conquered city, on a weary everlasting border-line.

And the Frenchman seemed far more weary, and also, more sensitive than the crude Alsatians.

She remembered the little street, the old, overhanging houses with black timbers and high gables. And like a great ghost, a reddish flush in its darkness, the uncanny cathedral breasting the oncomer, standing gigantic, looking down in darkness out of darkness, on the pigmy humanness of the city. It was built of reddish stone, that had a flush in the night, like dark flesh. And vast, an incomprehensibly tall, strange thing, it looked down out of the night. The great rose window, poised high, seemed like a breast of the vast Thing, and prisms and needles of stone shot up, as if it were plumage, dimly, half-visible in heaven.

There it was, in the upper darkness of the ponderous winter night, like a menace. She remembered, her spirit used in the past to soar aloft with it. But now, looming with a faint rust of blood out of the upper black heavens, the Thing stood suspended, looking down with vast, demonish menace, calm and implacable.

Mystery and dim, ancient fear came over the woman's soul. The cathedral looked so strange and demonish-heathen. And an ancient, indomitable blood seemed to stir in it. It stood there like some vast silent beast with teeth of stone, waiting, and wondering when to stoop against this pallid humanity.

And dimly she realized that behind all the ashy pallor and sulphur of our civilization, lurks the great blood-creature waiting, implacable and eternal, ready at last to crush our white brittleness and let the shadowy blood move erect once more, in a new implacable pride and strength. Even out of the lower heavens looms the great blood-dusky Thing, blotting out the Cross it was supposed to exalt.

The scroll of the night sky seemed to roll back, showing a huge, blood-dusky presence looming enormous, stooping, looking down, awaiting its moment.

* * *

In the great flat field of the Rhine plain, the shallow flood water was frozen, the furrows ran straight towards nowhere, the air seemed frozen, too, but the earth felt strong and barbaric, it seemed to vibrate, with its straight furrows, in a deep, savage undertone. There was the frozen savage thrill in the air also, something wild and unsubdued, pre-Roman.

This part of the Rhine valley, even on the right bank in Germany, was occupied by the French; hence the curious vacancy, the suspense, as if no men lived there, but some spirit was watching, watching over the vast, empty, straight-furrowed fields and the water-meadows. Stillness, emptiness, suspense, and a sense of something still impending.

A long wait in the station of Appenweier, on the main line of the Right-bank railway. The station was empty. Katherine remembered its excited, thrilling bustle in pre-war days.

"Yes," said the German guard to the station-master, "what do they hurry us out of Strasburg for, if they are only going to keep us so long here?"

The heavy Badisch German! The sense of resentful impotence in the Germans! Katherine smiled to herself. She realized that here the train left the occupied territory.

At last they set off, northwards, free for the moment, in

Germany. It was the land beyond the Rhine, Germany of the pine forests. The very earth seemed strong and unsubdued, bristling with a few reeds and bushes, like savage hair. There was the same silence, and waiting, and the old barbaric undertone of the white-skinned north, under the waning civilization. The audible overtone of our civilization seemed to be wearing thin, the old, low, pine-forest hum and roar of the ancient north seemed to be sounding through. At least, in Katherine's inner ear.

And there were the ponderous hills of the Black Forest, heaped and waiting sullenly, as if guarding the inner Germany. Black round hills, black with forest, save where white snow-patches of field had been cut out. Black and white, waiting there in the near distance, in sullen guard.

She knew the country so well. But not in this present mood, the emptiness, the sullenness, the heavy, recoiled waiting.

From *FANTASIA of THE UNCONSCIOUS*

It is half-rainy too—the wood so damp and still and so secret in the remote morning air. Morning, with rain in the sky, and the forest subtly brooding, and me feeling no bigger than a pea-bug between the roots of my fir. The trees seem so much bigger than me, so much stronger in life, prowling silent around. I seem to feel them moving and thinking and prowling, and they overwhelm me. Ah, well, the only thing is to give way to them.

It is the edge of the Black Forest—sometimes the Rhine far off, on its Rhine plain, like a bit of magnesium ribbon. But not to-day. To-day only trees, and leaves, and vegetable presences. Huge, straight fir-trees, and big beech-trees sending rivers of roots into the ground. And cuckoos, like noise falling in drops off the leaves. And me, a fool, sitting by a grassy wood-road with a pencil and a book, hoping to write more about that baby.

Never mind. I listen again for noises, and I smell the damp moss. The looming trees, so straight. And I listen for their silence—big, tall-bodied trees, with a certain magnificent cruelty about them—or barbarity—I don't know why I should say cruelty. Their magnificent, strong, round bodies! It almost seems I can hear the slow, powerful sap drumming in their trunks. Great full-blooded trees, with strange tree-blood in them, soundlessly drumming.

Trees that have no hands and faces, no eyes; yet the powerful sap-scented blood roaring up the great columns. A vast individual life, and an overshadowing will—the will of a tree; something that frightens you.

Suppose you want to look a tree in the face? You can't. It hasn't got a face. You look at the strong body of a trunk; you look above you into the matted body-hair of twigs and boughs; you see the soft green tips. But there are no eyes to look into, you can't meet its gaze. You keep on looking at it in part and parcel.

It's no good looking at a tree to know it. The only thing is to sit among the roots and nestle against its strong trunk, and not bother. That's how I write all about these planes and plexuses—between the toes of a tree, forgetting myself against the great ankle of the trunk. And then, as a rule, as a squirrel is stroked into its wickedness by the faceless magic of a tree, so am I usually stroked into forgetfulness, and into scribbling this book. My tree-book, really.

I come so well to understand tree-worship. All the old Aryans worshipped the tree. My ancestors. The tree of life. The tree of knowledge. Well, one is bound to sprout out some time or other, chip of the old Aryan block. I can so well understand tree-worship, and fear the deepest motive.

Naturally. This marvellous individual without a face, without lips or eyes or heart. This towering creature that never had a face. Here am I between his toes like a pea-bug, and him noiselessly over-reaching me, and I feel his great blood-jet surging. And he has no eyes. But he turns two ways: he thrusts himself tremendously down to the middle earth, where dead men sink in darkness, in the damp, dense undersoil; and he turns himself about in high air; whereas we have eyes on one side of our head only, and only grow upwards.

Plunging himself down into the black humus, with a root's gushing zest, where we can only rot dead; and his tips in high air, where we can only look up to. So vast and powerful and exultant in his two directions. And all the time he has no face, no thought: only a huge, savage, thoughtless soul. Where does he even keep his soul?—Where does anybody?

A huge, plunging, tremendous soul. I would like to be a tree for a while. The great lusts of roots. Root-lust. And no mind at all. He towers, and I sit and feel safe. I like to feel him towering round me. I used to be afraid. I used to fear their lust, their rushing black lust. But now I like it, I worship it. I always felt them huge primeval enemies, but now they are my only shelter and strength. I lose myself among the trees. I am so glad to be with them in their silent, intent passion, and their great lust. They feed my soul. But I can understand that Jesus was crucified on a tree.

INTERLUDE

LEAVING EUROPE

From *NOT I, BUT THE WIND*
by Frieda Lawrence

PERHAPS I can post this letter at Aden this evening, but we do not stop. We have come so far and so lovely. We stopped three hours in Port Said, and it was quite like the Thousand and One Nights. It was 9 o'clock in the morning, and the ladies of Port Said were all abroad shopping. Little black waddling heaps of black crêpe and two houri eyes between veil and mantle. Comic is the little peg that stands above the nose and keeps veil and headcloth together. There came a charabanc with twenty black women parcels. Then one of the women threw back her veil and spat at us because we are ugly Christians. But you still see everything—beggars, water carriers, the scribe who sits with his little table, and writes letters, the old one who reads the Koran, the men who smoke their " chibouks " in the open café and on the pavement—and what people! Beautiful Turks, Negroes, Greeks, Levantines, Fellaheen, three Bedouins out of the desert like animals, Arabs, wonderful. We have taken coal on board, and then at midday off again into the Suez Canal, and that is very interesting. The Canal is eighty-eight miles long, and you can only travel five miles an hour. There you sit in this great ship and you feel really on land, slowly travelling on a still land ship. The shores are quite near, you can surely throw an orange at the Arabs that work on the shores. Then you see beautifully, wonderfully, the Sahara *Wüste*, or desert—which do you say? The waterway goes narrow and alone through red-yellow sands. From time to time Arabs with camels work on the shores and keep on shouting "Hallo, Hallo" when the big ship passes so slowly. In the distance little sharp sand hills so red and pink-gold and sharp and the horizon sharp like a knife-edge so clear. Then a few lonely palms, lonely and lost in the strong light, small, like people that have not grown very tall.

Then again only sand, gold-pink and sharp little sand hills, so sharp and defined and clear, not like reality but a dream. Solemn evening came, and we so still, one thought we did not seem to move any more. Seagulls flew about like a sandstorm, and a great black bird of prey alone and cruel, so black between thousands of white screaming, quick-flying sea birds. Then we came to the Dead Sea, flat seas that extend very far, and slowly the sun sank behind the desert with marvellous colours, and as the sun had set, then such a sky like a sword burning green and pink. Beautiful it was, I have never seen anything so superhuman. One felt near to the doors of the old Paradise, I do not know how, but something only half human, something of a heaven with grey-browed, overbearing and cruel angels. The palm-trees looked so little, the angels should be much bigger and every one with a sword. Yes, it is a frontier country.

Next morning we were in the Red Sea. There stands Mount Sinai, red like old dried blood, naked like a knife and so sharp, so unnaturally sharp, like a dagger that has been dipped in blood and has dried long ago and is a bit rusty and is always there like something dreadful between man and his lost Paradise. All is Semitic and cruel, naked, sharp. No tree, no leaf, no life: the murderous will and the iron of the idea and ideal—iron will and ideal. So they stand, these dreadful shores of this Red Sea that is hot like an oven without air. It is a strange exit through this Red Sea—bitter. Behind lie finally Jerusalem, Greece, Rome and Europe, fulfilled and past—a great dreadful dream. It began with Jews and with Jews it ends. You should see Sinai, then you could know it. The ideal has been wicked against men and Jehovah is father of the ideal and Zeus and Jupiter and Christ are only sons. And God be praised Sinai and the Red Sea are past and consummated.

Yesterday morning we came through the Straits of Bab-el-Mandeb, again into the open. I am so glad that we came this way. Yesterday we always saw land—Arabia naked and desert but not so red and sharp and like dried blood. To-day we see no land but later on we shall pass Cape Socotra. This ship has gained fifteen hours. We are fifteen hours before time. Perhaps we arrive in Colombo on Sunday evening instead of Monday. It is very warm, but there is always air. The sea is covered with little white sea-horses, but the ship is still and sure. We have not had one single bad moment. All here on board so friendly and so good and comfortable. I work on the translation of *Maestro Don Gesualdo* and I let my inkpot fall on the deck. The *Osterley* shall wear my black sign for ever. At 11 o'clock in the morning we do not get Bovril any more, but ice cream. The women all wear colourful summer frocks. In the evening we dance. We see now the little flying fish. They are all silver and they fly like butterflies, so wee. There are also little black dolphins that run about like little black pigs.

AUSTRALIA

From *KANGAROO*

In which state of mind they jogged through the city, catching a glimpse from the top of a hill of the famous harbour spreading out with its many arms and legs. Or at least they saw one bay with warships and steamers lying between the houses and the wooded, bank-like shores, and they saw the centre of the harbour, and the opposite squat cliffs—the whole low wooded table-land reddened with suburbs and interrupted by the pale spaces of the many-lobed harbour. The sky had gone grey, and the low table-land into which the harbour intrudes squatted dark-looking and monotonous and sad, as if lost on the face of the earth: the same Australian atmosphere, even here within the area of huge, restless, modern Sydney, whose million inhabitants seem to slip like fishes from one side of the harbour to another.

Murdoch Street was an old sort of suburb, little squat bungalows with corrugated iron roofs, painted red. Each little bungalow was set in its own hand-breadth of ground, surrounded by a little wooden palisade fence. And there went the long street, like a child's drawing, the little square bungalows dot-dot-dot, close together and yet apart, like modern democracy, each one fenced round with a square rail fence. The street was wide, and strips of worn grass took the place of kerb-stones. The stretch of macadam in the middle seemed as forsaken as a desert, as the hansom clock-clocked along it.

Fifty-one had its name painted by the door. Somers had been watching these names. He had passed "Elite," and

"Très Bon" and "The Angels Roost" and "The Better 'Ole." He rather hoped for one of the Australian names, Wallamby or Wagga-Wagga. When he had looked at the house and agreed to take it for three months, it had been dusk, and he had not noticed the name. He hoped it would not be U-and-Me, or even Stella Maris.

* * *

Now he had tried Western Australia, and had looked at Adelaide and Melbourne. And the vast, uninhabited land frightened him. It seemed so hoary and lost, so unapproachable. The sky was pure, crystal pure and blue, of a lovely pale blue colour: the air was wonderful, new and unbreathed: and there were great distances. But the bush, the grey, charred bush. It scared him. As a poet, he felt himself entitled to all kinds of emotions and sensations which an ordinary man would have repudiated. Therefore he let himself feel all sorts of things about the bush. It was so phantom-like, so ghostly, with its tall pale trees and many dead trees, like corpses, partly charred by bush fires: and then the foliage so dark, like grey-green iron. And then it was so deathly still. Even the few birds seemed to be swamped in silence. Waiting, waiting—the bush seemed to be hoarily waiting. And he could not penetrate into its secret. He couldn't get at it. Nobody could get at it. What was it waiting for?

And then one night at the time of the full moon he walked alone in the bush. A huge electric moon, huge, and the tree-trunks like naked pale aborigines among the dark-soaked foliage, in the moonlight. And not a sign of life—not a vestige.

Yet something. Something big and aware and hidden! He walked on, had walked a mile or so into the bush, and had just come to a clump of tall, nude, dead trees, shining almost phosphorescent with the moon, when the terror of the bush overcame him. He had looked so long at the vivid moon, without thinking. And now, there was something among the trees, and his hair began to stir with terror, on his head. There was a presence. He looked at the weird, white, dead trees, and into the hollow distances of the bush. Nothing! Nothing at all. He turned to go home. And then immediately the hair on his scalp stirred and went icy cold with terror. What of? He knew quite well it was nothing. He knew quite well. But with his spine cold like ice, and the roots of his hair seeming to freeze, he walked on home, walked firmly and without haste. For he told himself he refused to be afraid, though he admitted the icy sensation of terror. But then to experience terror is not the same thing as to admit fear into the conscious soul. Therefore he refused to be afraid.

But the horrid thing in the bush! He schemed as to what it would be. It must be the spirit of the place. Something fully evoked to-night, perhaps provoked, by that unnatural West-Australian moon. Provoked by the moon, the roused spirit of the bush. He felt it was watching, and waiting. Following with certainty, just behind his back. It might have reached a long black arm and gripped him. But no, it wanted to wait. It was not tired of watching its victim. An alien people—a victim. It was biding its time with a terrible ageless watchfulness, waiting for a far-off end, watching the myriad intruding white men.

* * *

Richard S. had never quite got over that glimpse of terror in the Westralian bush. Pure foolishness, of course, but there's no telling where a foolishness may nip you. And, now that night had settled over Sydney, and the town and harbour were sparkling unevenly below, with reddish-seeming sparkles, whilst overhead the marvellous Southern Milky Way was tilting uncomfortably to the south, instead of crossing the zenith; the vast myriads of swarming stars that cluster all along the Milky Way, in the Southern sky, and the Milky Way itself leaning heavily to the south, so that you feel all on one side if you look at it; the Southern sky at night, with that swarming Milky Way all bushy with stars, and yet with black gaps, holes in the white star-road, while misty blotches of star-mist float detached, like cloud-vapours, in the side darkness, away from the road; the wonderful Southern night-sky, that makes a man feel so lonely, alien: with Orion standing on his head in the west, and his sword-belt upside-down, and his Dog-star prancing in mid-heaven, high above him; and with the Southern Cross insignificantly mixed in with the other stars, democratically inconspicuous; well then, now that night had settled down over Sydney, and all this was happening overhead for R. L. Somers and a few more people, our poet once more felt scared and anxious. Things seemed so different. Perhaps everything *was* different from all he had known. Perhaps if St. Paul and Hildebrand and Darwin had lived south of the equator, we might have known the world all different, quite different. But it is useless iffing.

* * *

The Somers now had neighbours: somewhat to the chagrin of Richard Lovat. He had come to this new country, the youngest country on the globe, to start a new life and flutter with a new hope. And he started with a rabid desire not to see anything and not to speak one single word to any single body—except Harriet, whom he snapped at hard enough. To be sure, the mornings sometimes won him over. They were so blue and pure: the blue harbour like a lake among the land, so pale blue and heavenly, with its hidden and half-hidden lobes intruding among the low, dark-brown cliffs, and among the dark-looking tree-covered shores, and up to the bright red suburbs. But the land, the ever-dark bush that was allowed to come to the shores of the harbour! It was strange that, with the finest of new air dimming to a lovely pale blue in the distance, and with the loveliest stretches of pale blue water, the tree-covered land should be so gloomy and lightless. It is the sun-refusing leaves of the gum-trees that are like dark, hardened flakes of rubber.

He was not happy, there was no pretending he was. He longed for Europe with hungry longing: Florence, with Giotto's pale tower: or the Pincio at Rome: or the woods in Berkshire—heavens, the English spring with primroses under the bare hazel bushes, and thatched cottages among plum blossom. He felt he would have given anything on earth to be in England. It was May—end of May—almost bluebell time, and the green leaves coming out on the hedges. Or the tall corn under the olives in Sicily. Or London Bridge, with all the traffic on the river. Or Bavaria with gentian and yellow globe flowers, and the Alps still icy. Oh God, to be in Europe, lovely, lovely Europe that he had hated so thoroughly and abused so vehemently, saying it was moribund and stale and finished. The fool was himself. He had got out of temper, and so had called Europe moribund: assuming that he himself, of course, was not moribund, but sprightly and chirpy and too vital, as the Americans would say, for Europe. Well, if a man wants to make a fool of himself, it is as well to let him.

Somers wandered disconsolate through the streets of Sydney, forced to admit that there were fine streets, like Birmingham for example; that the parks and the Botanical Gardens were handsome and well-kept; that the harbour, with all the two-decker brown ferry-boats sliding continuously from the Circular Quay, was an extraordinary place. But oh, what did he care about it all! In Martin Place he longed for Westminster, in Sussex Street he almost wept for Covent Garden and St. Martin's Lane, at the Circular Quay he pined for London Bridge. It was all London without being London. Without any of the lovely old glamour that invests London. This London of the Southern hemisphere was all, as it were, made in five minutes, a substitute for the real thing. Just a substitute—as margarine is a substitute for butter. And he went home to the little bungalow bitterer than ever, pining for England.

* * *

The road ended on the salt pool where the sea had ebbed in. Across was a state reserve—a bit of aboriginal Australia, with gum trees and empty spaces beyond the flat salt waters. Near at hand a man was working away, silently loading a boat with beach-sand, upon the lagoon. To the right the sea was rolling on the shore, and spurting high on some brown rocks. Two men in bathing-suits were running over the spit of sand from the lagoon to the surf, where two women in "waders," those rubber paddling-drawers into which we bundle our children at the seaside, were paddling along the fringe of the foam. A blond young man wearing a jacket over his bathing suit walked by with two girls. He had huge massive legs, astonishing. And near at hand Somers saw another youth lying on the warm sand-hill in the sun. He had rolled in the dry sand while he was wet, so he was hardly distinguishable. But he lay like an animal on his face in the sun, and again Somers wondered at the thick legs. They seemed to run to leg, these people. Three boys, one a lad of fifteen or so, came out of the warm lagoon in their bathing suits to roll in the sand and play. The big lad crawled on all fours and the little one rode on his back, and pitched off into the sand. They were extraordinarily like real young animals, mindless as opossums, lunging about.

This was Sunday afternoon. The sun was warm. The lonely man was just pushing off his boat on the lagoon. It sat deep in the water, half full of sand. Somers and Harriet lay on the sand-bank. Strange it was. And it *had* a sort of fascination. Freedom! That's what they always say. "You feel free in Australia." And so you do. There is a great relief in the atmosphere, a relief from tension, from pressure. An absence of control or will or form. The sky is open above you, and the air is open around you. Not the old closing-in of Europe.

But what then? The *vacancy* of this freedom is almost terrifying. In the openness and the freedom this new chaos, this litter of bungalows and tin cans scattered for miles and miles, this Englishness all crumbled out into formlessness and chaos. Even the heart of Sydney itself—an imitation of London and New York, without any core or pith of meaning. Business going on full speed: but only because it is the other end of English and American business.

The absence of any inner meaning: and at the same time the great sense of vacant spaces. The sense of irresponsible freedom. The sense of do-as-you-please liberty. And all utterly uninteresting. What is more hopelessly uninteresting than accomplished liberty? Great swarming, teeming Sydney flowing out into these myriads of bungalows, like shallow waters spreading, undyked. And what then? Nothing. No inner life, no high command, no interest in anything, finally.

* * *

The train ran for a long time through Sydney, or the endless outsides of Sydney. The town took almost as much leaving as London does. But it was different. Instead of solid rows of houses, solid streets like London, it was mostly innumerable detached bungalows and cottages, spreading for great distances, scattering over hills, low hills and shallow inclines. And then waste marshy places, and old iron, and abortive corrugated iron "works"—all like the Last Day of creation, instead of a new country. Away to the left they saw the shallow waters of the big opening where Botany Bay is: the sandy shores, the factory chimneys, the lonely places where it is still Bush. And the weary half-established straggling of more suburb.

"Como," said the station sign. And they ran on bridges over two arms of water from the sea, and they saw what looked like a long lake with wooded shores and bungalows: a bit like Lake Como, but oh, so unlike. That curious sombreness of Australia, the sense of oldness, with the forms all worn down low and blunt, squat. The squat-seeming earth. And then they ran at last into real country rather rocky, dark old rocks, and sombre bush with its different pale-stemmed dull-leaved gum-trees standing graceful, and various healthy-looking under-growth, and great spiky things like yuccas. As they turned south they saw tree-ferns standing on one knobbly leg among the gums, and among the rocks ordinary ferns and small bushes spreading in glades and up sharp hill-slopes. It was virgin bush, and as if unvisited, lost, sombre, with plenty of space, yet spreading grey for miles and miles, in a hollow towards the west. Far in the west, the sky having suddenly cleared, they saw the magical range of the Blue Mountains. And all this hoary space of bush between. The strange, as it were, *invisible* beauty of Australia, which is undeniably there, but which seems to lurk just beyond the range of our white vision. You feel you can't *see*—as if your eyes hadn't the vision in them to correspond with the outside landscape. For the landscape is so unimpressive, like a face with little or no features, a dark face. It is so aboriginal, out of our ken, and it hangs back so aloof. Somers always felt he looked at it through a cleft in the atmosphere; as one looks at one of the ugly-faced, distorted aborigines with his wonderful dark eyes that have such an incomprehensible ancient shine in them, across gulfs of unbridged centuries. And yet, when you don't have the feeling of ugliness or monotony, in landscape or in nigger, you get a sense of subtle, remote, *formless* beauty more poignant than anything ever experienced before.

* * *

The train jogged on again—they were there. The place was half and half. There were many tin roofs—but not *so* many. There were the wide, unmade roads running so straight as it were to nowhere, with little bungalow homes half-lost at the side. But they were pleasant little bungalow homes. Then quite near, inland, rose a great black wall of mountain, or cliff, or tor, a vast dark tree-covered tor that reminded Harriet of Matlock, only much bigger. The town trailed down from the foot of this mountain towards the railway, a huddle of grey and red-painted iron roofs. Then over the railway, towards the sea, it began again in a scattered, spasmodic fashion, rather forlorn bungalows and new " stores " and fields with rail fences, and more bungalows above the fields, and more still running down the creek shallows towards the hollow sea, which lay beyond like a grey mound, the strangest sight Harriet had ever seen.

Next to the railway was field, with men and youths playing football for their lives. Across the road from the football field was a barber's shop, where a man on horseback was leaning chattering to the barber, a young intelligent gentleman in eye-glasses. And on the broad grass of the roadside grew the trees with the bright scarlet flowers perching among the grey twigs.

Going towards the sea they were going away from the town that slid down at the bush-covered foot of the dark tor. The sun was just sinking to this great hill-face, amid a curdle of grey-white clouds. The faintest gold reflected in the more open eastern sky, in front. Strange and forlorn, the wide sandy-rutted road with the broad grass margin and just one or two bungalows. " Verdun " was the first, a wooden house painted dark red. But some had quite wide grass round them, inside their fences, like real lawns.

Victoria had to dart to the house-agent for the key. The other three turned to the left, up another wide road cut in the almost nothingness, past two straying bungalows perched on brick supports—then across a piece of grassland as yet unoccupied, where small boys were kicking a football—then round the corner of another new road, where water lay in a great puddle so that they had to climb on to the grass beside the fence of a big red-painted bungalow. Across the road was a big bungalow built with imitation timbered walls and a red corrugated roof and red huge water-tanks. The sea roared loudly, but was not in sight. Next along the forlorn little road nestled a real bright red-tiled roof among a high bushy hedge, and with a white gate.

* * *

A boy from the big red bungalow called to ask if he should bring milk across. The big red bungalow was a dairy. But Harriet followed eagerly on Jack's footsteps across the road. She peeped over the white gate as he unfastened it. A real lovely brick house, with a roof of bright red tiles coming down very low over dark wooden verandahs, and huge round rain-tanks, and a bit of grass and a big shed with double doors. Joy! The gate was open, and she rushed in, under the tall, over-leaning hedge that separated them from the neighbour, and that reached almost to touch the side of her house. A wooden side verandah with bedsteads—old rusty bedsteads patched with strip and rope—and then grass, a little front all of grass, with loose hedges on either side—and the sea, the great Pacific right there and rolling in huge white thunderous rollers not forty yards away, under her grassy platform of a garden. She walked to the edge of the grass. Yes, just down the low cliff, really only a bank, went her own little path, as down a steep bank, and then was smooth yellow sand, and the long sea swishing white up its incline, and rocks to the left, and incredible long rollers furling over and crushing down on the shore. At her feet! At her very feet, the huge rhythmic Pacific.

She turned to the house. There it crouched, with its long windows and its wide verandah and its various slopes of low, red-tiled roofs. Perfect! Perfect! The sun had gone down behind the great front of black mountain wall which she could still see over the hedge. The house inside was dark, with its deep verandahs like dark eyelids half closed. Somebody switched on a light. Long cottage windows, and a white ceiling with narrow dark beams. She rushed indoors. Once more in search of a home, to be alone with Lovat, where he would be happy. How the sea thundered!

* * *

The house had been let for seven months to a man and wife with eleven children. When Somers got up at sunrise, in the morning, he could well believe it. But the sun rose golden from a low fume of haze in the north-eastern sea. The waves rolled in pale and bluey, glass-green, wonderfully heavy and liquid. They curved with a long arch, then fell in a great, hollow thud and a spurt of white foam and a long, soft, snow-pure rush of forward flat foam. Somers watched the crest of fine, bristling spume fly back from the head of the waves as they turned and broke. The sea was all yellow-green light.

And through the light came a low, black tramp steamer, lurching up and down on the waves, disappearing altogether in the lustrous water, save for her bit of yellow-banded funnel and her mast-tips: then emerging like some long, out-of-shape dolphin on a wave-top. She was like some lost mongrel running over a furrowed land. She bellowed and barked forlornly, and hung round on the up-and-down waves.

Somers saw what she wanted. At the south end of the shallow bay was a long, high jetty straddling on great tree-trunk poles out on to the sea, and carrying a long line of little red coal-trucks, the sort that can be tipped up. Beyond the straddling jetty was a spit of low, yellow-brown land, grassy, with a stiff little group of trees like ragged Noah's ark trees, and farther in, a little farm-place with two fascinating big gum-trees that stuck out their clots of foliage in dark tufts at the end of slim, up-starting branches.

But the lines from the jetty ran inland for two hundred yards, to where a tiny colliery was pluming steam and smoke from beyond a marsh-like little creek. The steamer wanted to land. She saw the line of little trucks full and ready. She bellowed like a miserable cow, sloping up and down and turning round on the waters of the bay. Near the jetty the foam broke high on some sheltering rocks. The steamer seemed to watch yearningly like a dog outside a shut door. A little figure walked along the jetty, slowly, unconcernedly. The steamer bellowed again. The figure reached the end of the jetty, and hung out a red flag. Then the steamer shouted no more, but slowly, fearfully turned and slunk up and down the waves back towards Sydney.

The jetty—the forlorn pale-brown grassy bank running out to sea, with the clump of sharp, hard-pointed dark conifers, trees of the southern hemisphere, stiff and mechanical; then the foreshore with yellow sand and rollers; then two bungalows, and a bit of waste ground full of tins; that was the southern aspect. Northwards, next door, was the big imitation black and white bungalow, with a tuft of wind-blown trees and half-dead hedge between it and the Somers' house. That was north. And the sun was already sloping upwards and northwards. It gave Somers an uneasy feeling, the northward travelling of the climbing sun: as if everything had gone wrong. Inland, lit up dark-grey with its plumy trees in the morning light, was the great mountain or tor, with bare, greying rock showing near the top, and above the ridge-top the pure blue sky, so bright and absolutely unsullied, it was always a wonder. There was an unspeakable beauty about the mornings, the great sun from the sea, such a big, untamed, proud sun, rising up into a sky of such tender delicacy, blue, so blue, and yet so frail that even blue seems too coarse a colour to describe it, more virgin than humanity can conceive; the land inward lit up, the prettiness of many painted bungalows with tin roofs clustering up the low up-slopes of the grey-treed bush; and then rising like a wall, facing the light and still lightless, the tor face, with its high-up rim so grey, having tiny trees feathering against the most beautiful frail sky in the world. Morning!

But Somers turned to the house. It stood on one of the regulation lots, probably fifty feet by a hundred and fifty. The bit of level grass in front was only fifty feet wide, and perhaps about the same from the house to the brim of the sea-bank, which dropped bushily down some forty feet to the sand and the flat shore-rocks and the ocean. But this grassy garden was littered with bits of rag, and newspapers, sea-shells, tins and old sponges. And the lot next to it was a marvellous constellation of tin cans in every stage of rustiness, if you peeped between the bushes.

* * *

He lingered behind the rest, they were nearly home. They were at the wide sandy place where the creek left off. Its still, brackish waters just sank into the sands, without ever running to meet the waves. And beyond the sands was a sort of marsh, bushes and tall stark dead gum-trees, and a few thin-tufted trees. Half-wild ponies walked heavily from the bush to the sands, and across to the slope where the low cliff rose again. In the depths of the marsh-like level was the low chimney of the mine, and tips of roofs: and beyond, a long range of wire-like trees holding up tufts of foliage in handfuls, in front of the pale blue, diminishing range of the hills in the distance. It was a weird scene, full of definite detail, fascinating detail, yet all in the funeral-grey monotony of the bush.

Somers turned to the piled-up, white-fronted sea again. On the tip of a rock above him sat a little bird with hunched-up shoulders and a long beak: an absurd silhouette. He went towards it, talking to it. It seemed to listen to him: really to listen. That is another of the charms of Australia: the birds are not really afraid, and one can really communicate with them. In West Australia Somers could sit in the bush and talk to the flocks of big, handsome, black-and-white birds that they call magpies, but which are a sort of butcher bird, apparently. And they would gurgle little answers in their throats, and cock their heads on one side. Handsome birds they were, some with mottled grey breasts like fish. And the boldest would even come and take pieces of bread from his hands. Yet they were quite wild. Only they seemed to have a strange power of understanding the human psyche.

Now this little kingfisher by the sea. It sat and looked at Somers and cocked its head and listened. It *liked* to be talked to. When he came quite near, it sped with the straight low flight of kingfishers to another boulder, and waited for him. It was beautiful too: with a sheeny sea-green back and a pale breast touched with burnt yellow. A beautiful, dandy little fellow. And there he waited for Somers like a little penguin perching on a brown boulder. And Somers came softly near, talking quietly. Till he could almost touch the bird. Then away it sped a few yards, and waited. Sheeny greyish green, like the gum-leaves become vivid: and yellowish breast, like the suave gum-tree trunks. And listening, and waiting, and wanting to be talked to.

* * *

She loved to wake in the morning and open the bedroom door—they had the north bedroom, on the verandah, the room that had the sun all day long; then she liked to lie luxuriously in bed and watch the lovely, broken colours of the Australian dawn: always strange, mixed colours, never the primary reds and yellows. The sun rose on the north-east—she could hardly see it. But she watched the first yellow of morning, and then the strange, strong, smoky red-purple of floating pieces of cloud: then the rose and mist blue of the horizon, and the sea all reddish, smoky flesh-colour, moving under a film of gold like a glaze; then the sea gradually going yellow, going primrose, with the foam breaking blue as forget-me-nots or frost, in front. And on the near swing of the bluey primrose, sticking up through the marvellous liquid pale yellow glaze, the black fins of sharks. The triangular, black fins of sharks, like small, hard sails of hell-boats, amid the swimming luminousness. Then she would run out on the verandah. Sharks! Four or five sharks, skulking in the morning glow, and so near, she could almost have thrown bread to them. Sharks, slinking along quite near the coast, as if they were walking on the land. She saw one caught in the heave of a breaker, and lifted. And then she saw him start, saw the quick flurry of his tail as he flung himself back. The land to him was horror—as to her the sea, beyond that wall of ice-blue foam. She made Lovat come to look. He watched them slowly, holding the brush in his hand. He had made the fire, and was sweeping the hearth. Coffee was ready by the time Harriet was dressed: and he was crouching making toast. They had breakfast together on the front verandah, facing the sea, eastwards. And the sun slanted warm, though it was mid-winter, and the much-washed red-and-white tablecloth that had been in so many lands with them and that they used outdoors, looked almost too strongly coloured in the tender seeming atmosphere. The coffee had a lot of chicory in it, but the butter and milk were good, and the brownish honey, that also, like the landscape, tasted queer, as if touched with unkindled smoke. It seemed to Somers as if the people of Australia *ought* to be dusky. Think of Sicilian honey—like the sound of birds singing: and now this with a dusky undertone to it. But good too—so good!

* * *

There had been a squall in the night. At the tip of the rock-shelves above the waves men and youths, with bare, reddish legs, were fishing with lines for blackfish. They looked like animal creatures perching there, and like creatures they were passive or darting in their movements. A big albatross swung slowly down the surf: albatross or mollyhawk, with wide, waving wings.

The sea had thrown up, all along the surf-line, queer glittery creatures that looked like thin blown glass. They were bright transparent bladders of the most delicate ink-blue, with a long crest of deeper blue, and blind ends of translucent purple. And they had bunches of blue, blue strings, and one long blue string that trailed almost a yard across the sand, straight and blue and translucent. They must have been some sort of little octopus, with the bright glass bladder, big as smallish narrow pears, with a blue frill along the top to float them, and the strings to feel with—and perhaps the long string to anchor by. Who knows? Yet there they were, soft, brilliant, like pouches of frailest sea-glass. It reminded Somers of the glass they blow at Burano, at Venice. But there they never get the lovely soft texture and the colour.

The sky was tufted with cloud, and in the afternoon veils of rain swept here and there across the sea, in a changing wind. But then it cleared again, and Somers and Harriet walked along the sands, watching the blue sky mirror purple and the white clouds mirror warm on the wet sand. The sea talked and talked all the time, in its disintegrative, elemental language. And at last it talked its way into Somers's soul, and he forgot the world again, the babel. The simplicity came back, and with it the inward peace.

* * *

It was winter, but sunny, and hot walking. He climbed steadily up and up the highroad between the dense, damp jungle that grew at the base and up the steep rise of the tor-face, which he wanted to get to the top of. Strange birds made weird, metallic noises. Tree-ferns rose on their notchy little trunks, and great mosses tangled in with more ordinary bushes. Overhead rose the gum-trees, sometimes with great stark, dead limbs thrown up, sometimes hands over like pine-trees.

He sweated up the steep road till at last he came to the top. There, on the farther side, the dip slope, the hills sank and ran in spurs, all fairly densely wooded, but not like the scarp slope up which he had toiled. The scarp slope was jungle, impenetrable, with tree-ferns and bunchy cabbage-palms and mosses like bushes, a thick matted undergrowth beneath the boles of the trees. But the dip slope was bush: gum-trees rather scattered, and a low undergrowth like heath. The same lonely, unbreakable silence and loneliness that seemed to him the real bush. Curiously unapproachable to him. The mystery of the bush seems to recede from you as you advance, and then it is behind you if you look round. Lonely, and weird, and hoary.

He went on till he could look over the tor's edge at the land below. There was the scalloped sea-shore, for miles, and the strip of flat coast-land, sometimes a mile wide, sprinkled as far as the eye could reach with the pale-grey zinc roofs of the bungalows: all scattered like crystals in the loose cells of the dark tree-tissue of the shore. It was suggestive of Japanese landscape, dark trees and little, single, scattered toy houses. Then the bays of the shore, the coal-jetty, far off rocks down the coast, and long white lines of breakers.

But he was looking mostly straight below him, at the massed foliage of the cliff-slope. Down into the centre of the great, dull-green whorls of the tree-ferns, and on to the shaggy mops of the cabbage palms. In one place a long fall of creeper was yellowish with damp flowers. Gum-trees came up in tufts. The previous world!—the world of the coal age. The lonely, lonely world that had waited, it seemed, since the coal age. These ancient flat-topped tree-ferns, these tousled palms like mops. What was the good of trying to be an alert conscious man here? You couldn't. Drift, drift into a sort of obscurity, backwards into a nameless past, hoary as the country is hoary. Strange old feelings wake in the soul: old, non-human feelings. And an old, old indifference, like a torpor, invades the spirit. An old, saurian torpor. Who wins? There was the land sprinkled with dwellings as with granulated sugar. There was a black smoke of steamers on the high pale sea, and a whiteness of steam from a colliery among the dull trees. Was the land awake? Would the people waken this ancient land, or would the land put them to sleep, drift them back into the torpid semi-consciousness of the world of the twilight.

* * *

A queer bird sat hunched on a bough a few yards away, just below; a bird like a bunch of old rag, with a small rag of a dark tail, and a fluffy pale top like an owl, and a sort of frill round his neck. He had a long, sharp, dangerous beak. But he too was sunk in unutterable apathy. A kukooburra! Some instinct made him know that Somers was watching, so he just shuffled round on the bough and sat with his back to the man, and became utterly oblivious. Somers watched and wondered. Then he whistled. No change. Then he clapped his hands. The bird looked over its shoulder in surprise. What! it seemed to say. Is there somebody alive? Is that a live somebody?

It had quite a handsome face, with the exquisite long, dagger beak. It slowly took Somers in. Then he clapped again. Making an effort the bird spread quite big wings and whirred in a queer, flickering flight to a bough a dozen yards farther off. And there it clotted again.

Ah well, thought Somers, life is so big, and has such huge ante-worlds of grey twilight. How can one care about anything in particular!

* * *

The morning was one of the loveliest Australian mornings, perfectly golden, all the air pure, cold gold, the great gold effulgence to seaward, and the pure, cold pale-blue inland, over the dark range. The wind was blowing from inland, the sea was quiet as a purring cat with white paws, becoming darkish green-blue flecked with innumerable white flecks like rain-spots splashing the surface of a pool. The horizon was a clear and hard and dark sea against an almost white sky, but from far behind the horizon showed the mirage-magic tops of hazed, gold-white clouds, that seemed as if they indicated the far Pacific isles.

* * *

It was a wonderful Main Street, and, thank heaven, out of the wind. There were several large but rather scaring brown hotels, with balconies all round: there was a yellow stucco church with a red-painted tin steeple, like a weird toy: there were high roofs and low roofs, all corrugated iron: and you came to an opening, and there, behold, were one or two forlorn bungalows inside their wooden palings, and then the void. The naked bush, sinking in a hollow to a sort of marsh, and then down the coast some sort of "works," brick-works or something, smoking. All as if it had tumbled haphazard off the pantechnicon of civilization as it dragged round the edges of this wild land, and there lay, busy but not rooted in. As if none of the houses had any foundations.

Bright the sun, the air of marvellous clarity, tall stalks of cabbage palms rising in the hollow, and far off, tufted gum-trees against a perfectly new sky, the tufts at the end of wire branches. And farther off, blue, blue hills. In the Main Street, large and expensive motor-cars and women in fuzzy fur coats; long, quiescent Australian men in tired-out-looking navy blue suits trotting on brown ponies, with a carpet-bag in one hand, doing the shopping; girls in very much-made hats, also flirtily shopping; three boys with big, magnificent bare legs, lying in a sunny corner in the dust; a lonely white pony hitched as if for ever to a post at a street-corner.

"I like it," said Harriet. "It doesn't feel *finished*."

"Not even begun," he laughed.

But he liked it too: even the slumminess of some of the bungalows inside their wooden palings, drab-wood, decrepit houses, old tins, broken pots, a greeny-white pony reminding one of a mildewed old shoe, two half-naked babies sitting like bits of live refuse in the dirt, but with bonny, healthy bare legs: the awful place called "The Travellers' Rest—Mrs. Coddy's Boarding Home"—a sort of blind, squalid, corner-building made of wood and tin, with flat pieces of old lace-curtain nailed inside the windows, and the green blinds hermetically drawn. What must it have been like inside? Then an open space, and coral-trees bristling with red crest-flowers on their bare, cold boughs: and the hollow space of the open country, and the marvellous blue hills of the distance.

The wind was cold enough to make you die. Harriet was disgusted at having been dragged away from home. They trailed to the sea to try and get out of it, for it blew from the land, and the sun was hot. On the bay one lone man flinging a line into the water, on the edge of the conch-shaped, sloping sands. Dark-blue water, ruffled like mole-fur, and flicked all over with froth as with bits of feather-fluff. And many white gannets turning in the air like a snow-storm and plunging down into the water like bombs. And fish leaped in the furry water, as if the wind had turned them upside-down. And the gannets dropping and exploding into the wave, and disappearing. On the sea's horizon, so perfectly clear, a steamer like a beetle walking slowly along. Clear, with a non-earthly clarity.

* * *

He fled away to be by himself as much as he could. His great relief was the shore. Sometimes the dull exploding of the waves was too much for him, like hammer-strokes on the head. He tried to flee inland. But the shore was his great solace, for all that. The huge white rollers of the Pacific breaking in a white, soft, snow-rushing wall, while the thin spume flew back to sea like a combed mane, combed back by the strong, cold land-wind.

The thud, the pulse of the waves : that was his nearest throb of emotion. The other emotions seemed to abandon him. So suddenly, and so completely, to abandon him. So it was when he got back from Sydney and, in the night of moonlight, went down the low cliff to the sand. Immediately the great rhythm and ringing of the brakers obliterated every other feeling in his breast, and his soul was a moonlit hollow with the waves striding home. Nothing else.

And in the morning the yellow sea faintly crinkled by the inrushing wind from the land, and long, straight lines on the lacquered meadow, long, straight lines that reared at last in green glass, then broke in snow, and slushed softly up the sand. Sometimes the black, skulking fin of a shark. The water was very clear, very green, like bright green glass. Another big fish with humpy sort of fins sticking up, and horror, in the green water a big red mouth wide open. One day the fins of dolphin near, near, it seemed almost over the sea edge. And then, suddenly, oh wonder, they were caught up in the green wall of the rising water, and there for a second they hung in the watery, bright green pane of the wave, five big dark dolphins, a little crowd, with their sharp fins and blunt heads, a little sea-crowd in the thin, upreared sea. They flashed with a sharp black motion as the great wave curled to break. They flashed in-sea, flashed from the foamy horror of the land. And there they were, black little school, away in the lacquered water, panting, Richard imagined, with the excitement of the escape. Then one of the bold ducks came back to try again, and he jumped clean out of the water, above a wave, and kicked his heels as he dived in again.

The sea-birds were always wheeling : big, dark-backed birds

like mollyhawks and albatrosses with a great spread of wings: and the white gleaming gannets, silvery as fish in the air. In they went, suddenly, like bombs into the wave, spitting back the water. Then they slipped out again, slipped out of the ocean with a sort of sly exultance.

And ships walked on the wall-crest of the sea, shedding black smoke. A vast, hard, high sea, with tiny clouds like mirage islets away far, far back, beyond the edge.

So Richard knew it, as he sat and worked on the verandah, or sat at table in the room and watched through the open door. But it was usually in the afternoons he went down to it.

It was his afternoon occupation to go down to the sea's edge and wander slowly on the firm sand just at the foam-edge. Sometimes the great waves were turning like mill-wheels, white all down the shore. Sometimes they were smaller, more confused, as the current shifted. Sometimes his eyes would be on the sand, watching the wrack, the big bladder-weed thrown up, the little sponges like short clubs rolling in the wind, and once, only, those fairy blue wind-bags like bags of rainbow with long blue strings.

He knew all the places where the different shells were found, the white shells and the black and the red, the big rainbow scoops and the innumerable little black snails that lived on the flat rocks in the little pools. Flat rocks ran out near the coal jetty, and between them little creeks of black, round crunchy coal-pebbles: sea-coal. Sometimes there would be a couple of lazy, beach-combing men picking the biggest pebbles and putting them into sacks.

* * *

The sun was curving to the crest of the dark ridge. As soon as the sun went behind the ridge, shadow fell on the shore, and a cold wind came, he would go home. But he wanted the sun not to sink—he wanted the sun to stand still, for fear it might turn back to the soulful world where love is and the burden of bothering.

He saw something clutch in a pool. Crouching, he saw a horror—a dark-grey, brown-striped octopus thing with two smallish, white beaks or eyes, living in a cranny of a rock in a pool. It stirred the denser, viscous pool of itself and unfurled a long dark arm through the water, an arm studded with bright, orange-red studs or suckers. Then it curled the arm in again, cuddling close. Perhaps a sort of dark shore octopus, star-fish coloured amid its darkness. It was watching him as he crouched. He dropped a snail-shell near it. It huddled closer, and one of the beak-like white things disappeared; or were they eyes? Heaven knows. It eased out again, and from its dense jelly mass another thick dark arm swayed out, studded with the sea-orange studs. And he crouched and watched, while the white water hissed nearer to drive him away. Creatures of the sea! Creatures of the sea! The sea-water was round his boots, he rose with his hands in his pockets, to wander away.

The sun went behind the coal-dark hill, though the waves still glowed white-gold, and the sea was dark blue. But the shore had gone into shadow, and the cold wind came at once, like a creature that was lying in wait. The upper air seethed, seemed to hiss with light. But here was shadow, cold like the arm of the dark octopus. And the moon already in the sky.

Home again. But what was home? The fish has the vast ocean for home. And man has timelessness and nowhere. "I won't delude myself with the fallacy of home," he said to himself. "The four walls are a blanket I wrap around in, in timelessness and nowhere, to go to sleep."

* * *

Meanwhile he wandered round in the Australian spring. Already he loved it. He loved the country he had railed at so loudly a few months ago. While he "cared" he had to rail at it. But the care once broken inside him it had a deep mystery for him, and a dusky, far-off call that he knew would go on calling for long ages before it got any adequate response in human beings. From far off, from down long fern-dark avenues there seemed to be the voice of Australia, calling low.

He loved to wander in the bush at evening, when night fell so delicately yet with such soft mystery. Then the sky behind the trees was all soft, rose pink, and the great gum-trees ran up their white limbs into the air like quicksilver, plumed at the tips with dark tufts. Like rivulets the white boughs ran up from the white trunk; or like great nerves, with nerve-like articulations, branching into the dusk. Then he would stand under a tall fern-tree, and look up through the whorl of lace above his head, listening to the birds calling in the evening stillness, the parrots making a chinking noise.

Sitting at the edge of the bush he looked at the settlement and the sea beyond. He had quite forgotten how he used to grumble at the haphazard throwing of bungalows here and there and anywhere: how he used to hate the tin roofs, and the untidiness. It recalled to him the young Australian captain: "Oh, how I liked the rain on the tin roofs of the huts at the war. It reminded me of Australia."

"And now," thought Richard to himself, "tin roofs and scattered shanties will always remind me of Australia. They seem to me beautiful, though it's a fact they have nothing to do with beauty."

But, oh, the deep mystery of joy it was to him to sit at the edge of the bush as twilight fell, and look down at the township. The bungalows were built mostly on the sides of the slopes. They had no foundations, but stood on brickwork props, which brought them up to the level. There they stood on the hillsides, on their short legs, with darkness under their floors, the little bungalows, looking as if they weighed nothing. Looking flimsy, made of wood with corrugated zinc roofs. Some of them were painted dark red, roofs and all, some were painted grey, some were wooden simply. Many had the white-grey zinc roofs, pale and delicate. At the back was always one big water-butt of corrugated iron, a big round tank painted dark-red, the corrugation ribs running round, and a jerky, red-painted pipe coming down from the eaves. Sometimes there were two of these tanks: and a thin, not very tidy woman in a big straw hat stooping to the tap at the bottom of the tank. The roof came down low, making a long shade over the wooden verandahs. Nearly always a little loggia at the back, from which the house-door opened. And this little verandah was the woman's kitchen; there she had a little table with her dirty dishes, which she was going to wash up. And a cat would be trotting around, as if it had not an enemy in the world, while from the verandah a parrot called.

The bungalows near the bush edge had odd bits of garden nipped out of the paddocks and carefully railed in : then another little enclosure for the calf. At the back the earth was scratched, there was a rubbish heap of ashes and tins slipping into the brambles, and very white fowls clustering for bed-time. In front of the house, in another bit of garden with wooden palings, two camellia trees full of flowers, one white and one red, like artificial things, but a bit seared by the wind. And at the gate the branching coral trees still flowering flame from their dark, strong-thrusting, up-curving buds.

So, with evening falling. There were green roads laid out in the wild, with but one lost bungalow to justify them. And a lost horse wildly galloping round the corner of this blind road, to quiet down and look around. A belated collier galloping stiffly on his pony, out of the township, and a woman in a white blouse and black skirt, with two little girls beside her, driving a ramshackle little buggy with a quick-legged little pony, homewards through the trees.

Lights were beginning to glint out : the township was deciding it was night. The bungalows scattered far and wide, on the lower levels. There was a net-work of wide roads, or beginnings of roads. The heart of the township was one tiny bit of street a hundred yards long : Main Street. You knew where it was, as you looked down on the reddish earth and grass and bush, by the rather big roof of pale zinc and a sandy-coloured round gable of the hotel—the biggest building in the place. For the rest, it looked, from above, like an inch of street with tin roofs on either side, fizzling out at once into a wide grass-road with a few bungalows and then the bush. But there was the dark railway, and the little station. And then again the big paddocks rising to the sea, with a ridge of coral-trees and a farm-place. Richard could see Coo-ee with its low, red roof, right on the sea. Behind it the rail-fences of the paddocks, and the open grass, and the streets cut out and going nowhere, with an odd bungalow here and there.

So it was all round—a far and wide scattering of pale-roofed bungalows at random among grassy, cut-out streets, all along the levels above the sea, but keeping back from the sea, as if there were no sea. Ignoring the great Pacific. There were knolls and pieces of blue creek-hollow, blue of fresh-water in lagoons on the yellow sands. Up the knolls perched more bungalows, on very long front legs and no back legs, caves of dark underneath. And on the sky-line, a ridge of wiry trees with dark plume-tufts at the ends of the wires, and these little loose crystals of different-coloured, sharp-angled bungalows cropping out beneath. All in a pale, clear air, clear and yet far off, as it were visionary.

So the land swooped in grassy swoops, past the railway, steep up to the bush: here and there thick-headed palm-trees left behind by the flood of time and the flood of civilization both: bungalows with flame-trees: bare bungalows like packing-cases: an occasional wind-fan for raising water: a round well-pool, perfectly round: then the bush, and a little colliery steaming among the trees. And so the great tree-covered swoop upwards of the tor, to the red fume of clouds, red like the flame-flowers of sunset. In the darkness of trees the strange birds clinking and trilling: the tree-ferns with their knob-scaly trunks spreading their marvellous circle of lace overhead against the glow, the gum-trees like white, naked nerves running up their limbs, and the inevitable dead gum-trees poking stark grey limbs into the air. And the thick aboriginal dusk settling down.

* * *

There it is, laid all over the world, the heavy established European way of life. Like their huge ponderous cathedrals and factories and cities, enormous encumbrances of stone and steel and brick, weighing on the surface of the earth. They say Australia is free, and it is. Even the flimsy, foundationless bungalows. Richard railed at the scrappy amorphousness, till two nights he dreamed he was in Paris, and a third night it was in some other city of Italy or France. Here he was staying in a big palazzo of a house—and he struggled to get out, and found himself in a high old provincial street with old gable houses and dark shadow and himself in the gulf between: and at the end of the street a huge, pale-grey bulk of a cathedral, an old Gothic cathedral, huge and massive and grey and beautiful.

But, suddenly, the mass of it made him sick, and the beauty was nauseous to him. So strong a feeling that he woke up. And since that day he had been thankful for the amorphous scrappy scattering of foundationless shacks and bungalows. Since then he had loved the Australian landscape, with the remote gum-trees running their white nerves into the air, the random streets of flimsy bungalows, all loose from one another, and temporary seeming, the bungalows perched precariously on the knolls, like Japanese paper-houses, below the ridge of wire-and-tuft trees.

He had now a horror of vast super-incumbent buildings. They were a nightmare. Even the cathedrals. Huge, huge bulks that are called beauty. Beauty seemed to him like some turgid tumour. Never again, he felt, did he want to look at London, the horrible *weight* of it: or at Rome with all the pressure on the hills. Horrible, inert, man-moulded weight. Heavy as death.

No, no, the flimsy hills of Australia were like a new world, and the frail *inconspicuousness* of the landscape, that was still so clear and clean, clean of all fogginess or confusion: but the frail, aloof, inconspicuous clarity of the landscape was like a sort of heaven—bungalows, shacks, corrugated iron and all. No wonder Australians love Australia. It is the land that as yet has made no great mistake, humanly. The horrible human mistakes of Europe. And, probably, the even worse human mistakes of America.

* * *

In the newspapers Somers read of a big cyclone off the coast of China, which had engulfed thousands of Chinese. This cyclone was now travelling south, lashing its tail over the New Hebrides, and swooping its paws down the thousands of miles of east coast of Australia. The monster was expected to have spent itself by the time it reached Sydney. But it hadn't—not quite.

Down it came, in a great darkness. The sea began to have a strange yelling sound in its breakers, the black cloud came up like a wall from the sea, everywhere was dark. And the wind broke in volleys from the sea, and the rain poured as if the cyclone were a great bucket of water pouring itself endlessly down.

Richard and Harriet sat in the dark room at Coo-ee, with a big fire, and darkness raging in waters around. It was like the end of the world. The roaring snarl of the sea was of such volume, the volleying roar of the wind so great as to create almost a sense of silence in the room. The house was like a small cave under the water. Rain poured in waves over the dark room, and with a heaviness of spume. Though the roof came down so far and deep over the verandahs, yet the water swept in, and gurgled under the doors and in at the windows. Tiles were ripped off the verandah roof with a crash, and water splashed more heavily. For the first day there was nothing to do but to sit by the fire, and occasionally mop up the water at the seaward door. Through the long, low windows you saw only a yellow-livid fume, and over all the boom you heard the snarl of water.

* * *

These three days of dark wetness, slew, and wind finished her. On the second morning there was an abatement, and Richard rushed to the post. The boys, barefoot, bare-legged in the icy water, were running to school under mackintosh capes. Down came the rain in a wind suddenly like a great hose-pipe, and Richard got home a running, streaming pillar of water. Home into the dark room and the sulky tiger of Harriet.

The storm went on, black, all day, all night, and the next day the same, inside the house as well as out. Harriet sulked the more like a frenzied sick tigress. The afternoon of the third day another abatement into light rain, so Richard pulled on thick boots and went out to the shore. His grass was a thin surface stream, and down the low cliffs, one cascade stream. The sea was enormous: wave after wave in immediate succession, raving yellow and crashing dull into the land. The yeast-spume was piled in hills against the cliffs, among the big rocks, and in swung the raving yellow water, in great dull blows under the land, hoarsely surging out of the dim yellow blank of the sea. Harriet looked at it for a few moments, shuddering and peering down like a sick tigress in a flood. Then she turned tail and rushed indoors.

Richard tried to walk under the cliffs. But the whole shore was ruined, changed: a whole mass of new rocks, a chaos of heaped boulders, a gurgle of rushing, clayey water, and heaps of collapsed earth.

On the fourth day the wind had sunk, the rain was only thin, the dark sky was breaking. Gradually the storm of the sky went down. But not the sea. Its great yellow fore-fringe was a snarl of wave after wave, unceasing. And the shore was a ruin. The beach seemed to have sunk or been swept away, the shore was a catastrophe of rocks and boulders. Richard scrambled along through the dank wetness to a bit of sand, where sea-weed was piled like bushes, and he could more or less walk. But soon he came to a new obstacle. The creek, which formerly had sunk at the edge of the beach in a long pool, and left the sloping sand all free and beautiful, had now broken through, levelled the sand, and swept in a kind of snarling river to the snarling waves, across the cut-out sand. The fresh-water met the waves with a snarl, and sometimes pushed on into the sea, sometimes was shoved back and heaped up with a rattle of angry protest. Waters against waters.

The beach never recovered, during the Somers' stay, the river never subsided into the sand, the sandy foreshore never came back. It was a rocky, boulder-heaped ruin with that stream for an impasse. Harriet would not go down to the sea any more. The waves still raved very high, they would not go back, and they lashed with a venomousness to the cliffs, to cut a man off. Richard would wander cold and alone on this inhospitable shore, looking for shells, out of the storm. And all the time the waves would lash up, and he would scramble out. It seemed to him female and vindictive. "Beastly water, beastly water, rolling up so high. Beastly water, beastly water, rolling up so high, breaking all the shells just where they lie"—he crooned to himself, crooning a kind of war-croon, malevolent against the malevolence of this ocean.

* * *

Nothing is lovelier than to drive into the Australian bush in spring, on a clear day: and most days are clear and hot. Up the steep climb the tree-ferns and the cabbage-palms stood dark and unlighted as ever, among the great gums. But once at the top, away from the high road and the sea-face, trotting on the yellow-brown sandy trail through the sunny, thinly scattered trees of the untouched bush, it was heaven. They splashed through a clear, clear stream, and walked up a bank into the nowhere, the pony peacefully marching.

The bush was in bloom, the wattles were out. Wattle, or mimosa, is the national flower of Australia. There are said to be thirty-two species. Richard found only seven as they wandered along. The little, pale, sulphur wattle with a reddish stem sends its lovely sprays so aerial out of the sand of the trail, only a foot or two high, but such a delicate, spring-like thing. The thorny wattle with its fuzzy pale balls tangles on the banks. Then beautiful heath-plants with small bells, like white heather, stand in tall, straight tufts, and above them the gold sprays of the intensely gold bush mimosa, with here and there, on long, thin stalks like hairs almost, beautiful blue flowers, with gold grains, three-petalled, like reed-flowers, and blue, blue with a touch of Australian darkness. Then comes a hollow, desolate bare place with empty greyness and a few dead, charred gum-trees, where there has been a bush-fire. At the side of this bare place great flowers, twelve feet high, like sticky dark lilies in bulb-buds at the top of the shaft, dark, blood-red. Then over another stream, and scattered bush once more, and the last queer, gold-red bushes of the bottle-bush tree, like soft-bristly golden bottle-brushes standing stiffly up, and the queer black-boys on one black leg with a tuft of dark-green spears, sending up the high stick of a seed-stalk, much taller than a man. And here and there the gold bushes of wattle with their narrow dark leaves.

Richard turned and they plunged into the wild grass and

strange bushes, following the stream. By the stream the mimosa was all gold, great gold bushes full of spring fire rising over your head, and the scent of the Australian spring, and the most ethereal of all golden bloom, the plumy, many-balled wattle, and the utter loneliness, the manlessness, the untouched blue sky overhead, the gaunt, lightless gum-trees rearing a little way off, and sound of strange birds, vivid ones of strange, brilliant birds that flit round. Save for that, and for some weird frog-like sound, indescribable, the age-unbroken silence of the Australian bush.

But it is wonderful, out of the sombreness of gum-trees, that seem the same, hoary for ever, and that are said to begin to wither from the centre the moment they are mature—out of the hollow bush of gum-trees and silent heaths, all at once, in spring, the most delicate feathery yellow of plumes and plumes and plumes and trees and bushes of wattle, as if angels had flown right down out of the softest gold regions of heaven to settle here, in the Australian bush. And the perfume in all the air that might be heaven, and the unutterable stillness, save for strange bright birds and flocks of parrots, and the motionlessness, save for a stream and butterflies and some small brown bees. Yet a stillness, and manlessness, and an elation, the bush flowering at the gates of heaven.

Somers and Harriet left the pony and clambered along the stream, past trees of grey, feathery-leaved wattle, most sumptuous of all in soft gold in the sky, and bushes of the grey-hard, queer-leaved wattle, on to the thick green of strange trees narrowing into the water. The water slithered rushing over steep rocks. The two scrambled down, and along after the water, to an abrupt edge. There the water fell in a great roar down a solid rock, and broke and rushed into a round, dark pool, dark, still fathomless, low down in a gruesome dark cup in the bush, with rocks coming up to the trees. In this tarn the stream disappeared. There was no outlet. Rock and bush shut it in. The river just dived into the ground.

It was a dark, frightening place, famous for snakes. Richard hoped the snakes were still sleeping. But there was a horror of them in the air, rising from the tangled undergrowth, from under the fallen trees, the gum-trees that crashed down into the great ferns, eaten out by white ants.

In this place already the Christmas bells were blooming, like some great heath with hanging, bright red bells tipped with white. Other more single bell-flowers, a little bit like foxgloves, but stiff and sharp. All the flowers stiff, sharp, like crystals of colour come opaque out of the sombre, stiff, bristly bush plants.

Harriet had armfuls of bloom, gold plumage of many branches of different wattles, and the white heather, the scarlet bells, with the deep-blue reed-blobs. The sulky with all the bloom looked like a corner of paradise. And as they trotted home through the bush evening was coming, the gold sun slanting. But Richard kept jumping out from among the flowers, to plunge into the brake for a new flower. And the little pony looked round watching him impatiently and displeased. But it was a gentle, tolerant, Australian little beast, with untold patience. Only Harriet was frightened of the coming dusk.

So at length they were slipping down the steep slopes again, between the dense, creeper-tangled jungle and tree-ferns, dark, chilly. They passed a family moving from nowhere to nowhere, two colts trotting beside the wagon. And they came out at last at the bottom, to the lost, flickering little township, at nightfall.

* * *

So, it was time to take out handkerchiefs and wave across space. Few people wept. Somers waved and waved his orange silk kerchief in the blue air. Farewell! Farewell! Farewell Victoria and Jaz's wife, farewell Australia, farewell Britain and the great Empire. Farewell! Farewell! The last streamers blowing away, like broken attachments, broken heart-strings. The crowd on the wharf gone tiny in the sun, and melting away as the ship turned.

Richard watched the Observatory go by: then the Circular Quay, with all its ferry-wharves, and a Nippon steamer lying at her berth, and a well-known, big buff and black P. and O. boat at the P. and O. wharf, looking so like India. Then that was gone too, and the Governor's Palace, and the castellated Conservatorium of Music on its hill, where Richard had first seen Jack—the Palace Gardens, and the blue inlet where the Australian " Fleet " lay comfortably rusting. Then they drifted across harbour, nearer to the wild-seeming slope, like bush, where the Zoo is. And then they began to wait, to hang round.

There ahead was the open gate of the harbour, the low Heads with the South Lighthouse, and the Pacific beyond, breaking white. On the left was Manly, where Harriet had lost her yellow scarf. And then the tram going to Narrabeen, where they had first seen Jaz. Behind was the great lobed harbour so blue, and Sydney rather inconspicuous on the south hills, with its one or two skyscrapers. And already, the blue water all round, and a thing of the past.

It was midday before they got out of the Heads, out of the harbour into the open sea. The sun was hot, the wind cold. There were not very many passengers in the first-class: and nobody who looked possible to the Somers pair. Richard sat in the sun watching the dark coast of Australia, so sombre, receding. Harriet watched the two seamen casting rubbish overboard: such a funny assortment of rubbish. The iron sank in the deep, dark water, the wood and straw and cardboard drearily floated. The low Sydney Heads were not far off.

Lovat watched till he could see the dark of the mountain, far away, behind Coo-ee. He was almost sure of the shape. He thought of the empty house—the sunny grass in front—the sunny foreshore with its new rocks—the township behind, the dark tor, the bush, the Australian spring. The sea seemed dark and cold and inhospitable.

It was only four days to New Zealand, over a cold, dark, inhospitable sea.

From *THE WOMAN WHO RODE AWAY*

SHE set off without a qualm, riding astride on her strong roan horse, and wearing a riding-suit of coarse linen, a riding-skirt over her linen breeches, a scarlet neck-tie over her white blouse, and a black felt hat on her head. She had food in her saddle-bags, an army canteen with water, and a large, native blanket tied on behind the saddle. Peering into the distance, she set off from her home. Manuel and the little boy stood in the gateway to watch her go. She did not even turn to wave them farewell.

But when she had ridden about a mile, she left the wild road and took a small trail to the right, that led into another valley, over steep places and past great trees, and through another deserted mining-settlement. It was September, the water was running freely in the little stream that had fed the now-abandoned mine. She got down to drink, and let the horse drink too.

She saw natives coming through the trees, away up the slope. They had seen her, and were watching her closely. She watched in turn. The three people, two women and a youth, were making a wide detour, so as not to come too close to her. She did not care. Mounting, she trotted ahead up the silent valley, beyond the silver-works, beyond any trace of mining. There was still a rough trail, that led over rocks and loose stones into the valley beyond. This trail she had already ridden, with her husband. Beyond that she knew she must go south.

Curiously she was not afraid, although it was a frightening country, the silent, fatal-seeming mountain-slopes, the occasional distant, suspicious, elusive natives among the trees, the great carrion birds occasionally hovering, like great flies, in the distance, over some carrion or some ranch house or some group of huts.

As she climbed, the trees shrank and the trail ran through a thorny scrub, that was trailed over with blue convolvulus and an occasional pink creeper. Then these flowers lapsed. She was nearing the pine-trees.

She was over the crest, and before her another silent, void, green-clad valley. It was past midday. Her horse turned to a little runlet of water, so she got down to eat her midday meal. She sat in silence looking at the motionless unliving valley, and at the sharp-peaked hills, rising higher to rock and pine-trees, southwards. She rested two hours in the heat of the day, while the horse cropped around her.

Curious that she was neither afraid nor lonely. Indeed, the loneliness was like a drink of cold water to one who is very thirsty. And a strange elation sustained her from within.

She travelled on, and camped at night in a valley beside a stream, deep among the bushes. She had seen cattle and had crossed several trails. There must be a ranch not far off. She heard the strange wailing shriek of a mountain-lion, and the answer of dogs. But she sat by her small camp fire in a secret hollow place and was not really afraid. She was buoyed up always by the curious, bubbling elation within her.

It was very cold before dawn. She lay wrapped in her blanket looking at the stars, listening to her horse shivering, and feeling like a woman who has died and passed beyond. She was not sure that she had not heard, during the night, a great crash at the centre of herself, which was the crash of her own death. Or else it was a crash at the centre of the earth, and meant something big and mysterious.

With the first peep of light she got up, numb with cold, and made a fire. She ate hastily, gave her horse some pieces of oilseed cake, and set off again. She avoided any meeting—and since she met nobody, it was evident that she in turn was avoided. She came at last in sight of the village of Cuchitee, with its black houses with their reddish roofs, a sombre, dreary little cluster below another silent, long-abandoned mine. And beyond, a long, great mountain-side, rising up green and light to the darker, shaggier green of pine-trees. And beyond the pine-trees stretches of naked rock against the sky, rock slashed already and brindled with white stripes of snow. High up, the new snow had already begun to fall.

* * *

The sun was setting, a great yellow light flooded the last of the aspens, flared on the trunks of the pine-trees, the pine-needles bristled and stood out with dark lustre, the rocks glowed with unearthly glamour. And through this effulgence the Indian at her horse's head trotted unweariedly on, his dark blanket swinging, his bare legs glowing with a strange transfigured ruddiness in the powerful light, and his straw hat with its half-absurd decorations of flowers and feathers shining showily above his river of long black hair. At times he would utter a low call to the horse, and then the other Indian, behind, would fetch the beast a whack with the stick.

The wonder-light faded off the mountains, the world began to grow dark, a cold air breathed down. In the sky, half a moon was struggling against the glow in the west. Huge shadows came down from steep rocky slopes. Water was rushing. The woman was conscious only of her fatigue, her unspeakable fatigue, and the cold wind from the heights. She was not aware how moonlight replaced daylight. It happened while she travelled unconscious with weariness.

From *ST. MAWR*

It was autumn, and the loveliest time in the south-west, where there is no spring, snow blowing into the hot lap of summer; and no real summer, hail falling in thick ice, from the thunderstorms: and even no very definite winter, hot sun melting the snow and giving an impression of spring at any time. But autumn there is, when the winds of the desert are almost still, and the mountains fume no clouds. But morning comes cold and delicate, upon the wild sunflowers and the puffing, yellow-flowered greasewood. For the desert blooms in autumn. In spring it is grey ash all the time, and only the strong breath of the summer sun, and the heavy splashing of thunder rain succeeds at last, by September, in blowing it into soft, puffy yellow fire.

It was such a delicate morning when Lou drove out with Phœnix towards the mountains, to look at this ranch that a Mexican wanted to sell. For the brief moment the high mountains had lost their snow: it would be back again in a fortnight: and stood dim and delicate with autumn haze. The desert stretched away pale, as pale as the sky, but silvery and sere with hummock-mounds of shadow, and long wings of shadow, like the reflection of some great bird. The same eagle-shadows came like rude paintings of the outstretched bird, upon the mountains, where the aspens were turning yellow. For the moment, the brief moment, the great desert-and-mountain landscape had lost its certain cruelty, and looked tender, dreamy. And many, many birds were flickering around.

* * *

Her cabin faced the slow downslope of the clearing, the alfalfa field: her long, low cabin, crouching under the great pine-tree that threw up its trunk sheer in front of the house in the yard. That pine-tree was the guardian of the place. But a bristling, almost demonish guardian, from the far-off crude ages of the world. Its great pillar of pale, flakey-ribbed copper rose there in strange callous indifference, and the grim permanence which is in pine-trees. A passionless, non-phallic column, rising in the shadows of the pre-sexual world, before the hot-blooded ithyphallic column ever erected itself. A cold, blossomless, resinous sap surging and oozing gum, from that pallid brownish bark. And the wind hissing in the needles, like a vast nest of serpents. And the pine cones falling plumb as the hail hits them. Then lying all over the yard, open in the sun like wooden roses, but hard, sexless, rigid with a blind will.

Past the column of that pine-tree, the alfalfa field sloped gently down, to the circling guard of pine-trees, from which silent, living barrier isolated pines rose to ragged heights at intervals, in blind assertiveness. Strange, those pine-trees! In some lights all their needles glistened like polished steel, all subtly glittering with a whitish glitter among darkness, like real needles. Then again, at evening, the trunks would flare up orange red, and the tufts would be dark alert tufts like a wolf's tail touching the air. Again, in the morning sunlight they would be soft and still, hardly noticeable. But all the same, present, and watchful. Never sympathetic, always watchfully on their guard, and resistant, they hedged one in with the aroma and the power and the slight horror of the pre-sexual primeval world. The world where each creature was crudely limited to its own ego, crude and bristling and cold, and then crowding in packs like pine-trees and wolves.

But beyond the pine-trees, ah, there beyond, there was beauty for the spirit to soar in. The circle of pines, with the loose trees rising high and ragged at intervals, this was the barrier, the fence to the foreground. Beyond was only distance, the desert a thousand feet below, and beyond.

The desert swept its great fawn-coloured circle around, away beyond and below like a beach, with a long mountain-side of pure blue shadow closing in the near corner, and strange bluish hummocks of mountains rising like wet rock from a vast strand, away in the middle distance, and beyond, in the farthest distance, pale blue crests of mountains looking over the horizon, from the west, as if peering in from another world altogether.

Ah, that was beauty!—perhaps the most beautiful thing in the world. It was pure beauty, *absolute* beauty! There! That was it. To the little woman from New England, with her tense, fierce soul and her egoistic passion of service, this beauty was absolute, a *ne plus ultra*. From her doorway, from her porch, she could watch the vast, eagle-like wheeling of the daylight, that turned as the eagles which lived in the near rocks turned overhead in the blue, turning their luminous, dark-edged-patterned bellies and underwings upon the pure air, like winged orbs. So the daylight made the vast turn upon the desert, brushing the farthest outwatching mountains. And sometimes, the vast strand of the desert would float with curious undulations and exhalations amid the blue fragility of the mountains, whose upper edges were harder than the floating bases. And sometimes she would see the little brown adobe houses of the village Mexicans, twenty miles away, like little cube crystals of insect-houses dotting upon the desert, very distinct, with a cotton-wood tree or two rising near. And sometimes she would see the far-off rocks, thirty miles away, where the canyon made a gateway between the mountains. Quite clear, like an open gateway out of a vast yard, she would see the cut-out bit of the canyon passage. And on the desert itself, curious puckered folds of mesa-sides. And a blackish crack which in places revealed the otherwise invisible canyon of the Rio Grande. And beyond everything, the mountains like icebergs showing up from an outer sea. Then later, the sun would go down blazing above the shallow cauldron of simmering darkness, and the round mountain of Colorado would lump up into uncanny significance, northwards. That was always rather frightening. But morning came again, with the sun peeping over the mountain slopes and lighting the desert away in the distance long, long before it lighted on her yard. And then she would see another valley, like magic and very lovely, with green fields and long tufts of cotton-wood trees, and a few long-cubical adobe houses, lying floating in shallow light below, like a vision.

Ah! it was beauty, beauty absolute, at any hour of the day: whether the perfect clarity of morning, or the mountains beyond the simmering desert at noon, or the purple lumping of northern mounds under a red sun at night. Or whether the dust whirled in tall columns, travelling across the desert far away, like pillars of cloud by day, tall, leaning pillars of dust hastening with ghostly haste: or whether, in the early part of the year, suddenly in the morning a whole sea of solid white would rise rolling below, a solid mist from melted snow, ghost-white under the mountain sun, the world below blotted out: or whether the black rain and cloud streaked down, far across the desert, and lightning stung down with sharp white stings on the horizon: or the cloud travelled and burst overhead, with rivers of fluid blue fire running out of heaven and exploding on earth, and hail coming down like a world of ice shattered above: or the hot sun rode in again: or snow fell in heavy silence: or the world was blinding white under a blue sky, and one must hurry under the pine-trees for shelter against that vast, white, back-beating light which rushed up at one and made one almost unconscious, amid the snow.

It was always beauty, *always*! It was always great, and splendid, and, for some reason, natural. It was never grandiose or theatrical. Always, for some reason, perfect. And quite simple, in spite of it all.

So it was, when you watched the vast and living landscape. The landscape lived, and lived as the world of the gods, unsullied and unconcerned. The great circling landscape lived its own life, sumptuous and uncaring. Man did not exist for it.

* * *

The wild life, even the life of the trees and flowers, seemed one bristling, hair-raising tussle. The very flowers came up bristly, and many of them were fang-mouthed, like the dead-nettle: and none had any real scent. But they were very fascinating, too, in their very fierceness. In May, the curious columbines of the stream-beds, columbines scarlet outside and yellow in, like the red and yellow of a herald's uniform—farther from the dove nothing could be: then the beautiful rosy-blue of the great tufts of the flower they called bluebell, but which was really a flower of the snap-dragon family: these grew in powerful beauty in the little clearing of the pine-trees, followed by the flower the settlers had mysteriously called herb honey-suckle: a tangle of long drops of pure fire-red, hanging from slim invisible stalks of smoke colour. The purest, most perfect vermilion scarlet, cleanest fire-colour, hanging in long drops like a shower of fire-rain that is just going to strike the earth. A little later, more in the open, there came another sheer fire-red flower, sparking, fierce red stars running up a bristly grey ladder, as if the earth's fire-centre had blown out some red sparks, white-speckled and deadly inside, puffing for a moment in the dry air.

So it was! The alfalfa field was one raging, seething conflict of plants trying to get hold. One dry year, and the bristly wild things had got hold: the spiky, blue-leaved thistle-poppy with its moon-white flowers, the low clumps of blue nettle-flower, the later rush, after the sereneness of June and July, the rush of red sparks and michaelmas daisies, and the tough wild sunflowers, strangling and choking the dark, tender green of the clover-like alfalfa! A battle, a battle, with banners of bright scarlet and yellow.

When a really defenceless flower did issue, like the moth-still, ghost-centred mariposa lily, with its inner moth-dust of yellow, it came invisible. There was nothing to be seen, but a hair of greyish grass near the oak-scrub. Behold, this invisible long stalk was balancing a white, ghostly, three-petalled flower, naked out of nothingness. A mariposa lily!

Only the pink wild roses smelled sweet, like the old world. They were sweet-briar roses. And the dark blue hare-bells among the oak-scrub, like the ice-dark bubbles of the mountain flowers in the Alps, the Alpen-glocken.

The roses of the desert are the cactus flowers, crystal of translucent yellow or of rose-colour. But set among spines the devil himself must have conceived in a moment of sheer ecstasy.

Nay, it was a world before and after the God of Love. Even the very humming-birds hanging about the flowering squawberry bushes, when the snow had gone, in May, they were before and after the God of Love. And the blue jays were crested dark with challenge, and the yellow-and-dark woodpecker was fearless like a warrior in war-paint, as he struck the wood. While on the fence the hawks sat motionless, like dark fists clenched under heaven, ignoring man and his ways.

Summer, it was true, unfolded the tender cotton-wood leaves, and the tender aspen. But what a tangle and a ghostly aloofness in the aspen thickets high up on the mountains, the coldness that is in the eyes and the long cornelian talons of the bear.

Summer brought the little wild strawberries, with their savage aroma, and the late summer brought the rose-jewel raspberries in the valley cleft. But how lonely, how harsh-lonely and menacing it was, to be alone in that shadowy, steep cleft of a canyon just above the cabins, picking raspberries, while the thunder gathered thick and blue-purple at the mountain tops. The many wild raspberries hanging rose-red in the thickets. But the stream bed below all silent, waterless. And the trees all bristling in silence, and waiting like warriors at an outpost. And the berries waiting for the sharp-eyed, cold, long-snouted bear to come rambling and shaking his heavy sharp fur.

* * *

She rode on, and emerged at length in the lap of the summit. Beyond her was a great concave of stone and stark, dead-grey trees, where the mountain ended against the sky. But nearer was the dense black, bristling spruce, and at her feet was the lap of the summit, a flat little valley of sere grass and quiet-standing yellow aspens, the stream trickling like a thread across.

It was a little valley or shell from which the stream was gently poured into the lower rocks and trees of the canyon. Around her was a fairy-like gentleness, the delicate sere grass, the groves of delicate-stemmed aspens dropping their flakes of bright yellow. And the delicate, quick little stream threading through the wild, sere grass.

Here one might expect deer and fawns and wild things, as in a little paradise. Here she was to wait for Romero, and they were to have lunch.

She unfastened her saddle and pulled it to the ground with a crash, letting her horse wander with a long rope. How beautiful Tansy looked, sorrel, among the yellow leaves that lay like a patina on the sere ground. The Princess herself wore a fleecy sweater of a pale, sere buff, like the grass, and riding-breeches of a pure orange-tawny colour. She felt quite in the picture.

From her saddle pouches she took the packages of lunch, spread a little cloth, and sat to wait for Romero. Then she made a little fire. Then she ate a devilled egg. Then she ran after Tansy, who was straying across-stream. Then she sat in the sun, in the stillness near the aspens, and waited.

The sky was blue. Her little alp was soft and delicate as fairy-land. But beyond and up jutted the great slopes, dark with the pointed feathers of spruce, bristling with grey dead trees among grey rock, or dappled with dark and gold. The beautiful, but fierce, heavy, cruel mountains, with their moments of tenderness.

She saw Tansy start, and begin to run. Two ghost-like figures on horseback emerged from the black of the spruce across the stream. It was two Indians on horseback, swathed like seated mummies in their pale-grey cotton blankets. Their guns jutted beyond the saddles. They rode straight towards her, to her thread of smoke.

As they came near, they unswathed themselves and greeted her, looking at her curiously from their dark eyes. Their black hair was somewhat untidy, the long rolled plaits on their shoulders were soiled. They looked tired.

They got down from their horses near her little fire—a camp was a camp—swathed their blankets round their hips, pulled the saddles from their ponies and turned them loose, then sat down. One was a young Indian whom she had met before, the other was an older man.

"You all alone?" said the younger man.

* * *

She took a saucepan and went down the stones to the water. It was very still and mysterious, and of a deep green colour, yet pure, transparent as glass. How cold the place was! How mysterious and fearful.

She crouched in her dark cloak by the water, rinsing the saucepan, feeling the cold heavy above her, the shadow like a vast weight upon her, bowing her down. The sun was leaving the mountain tops, departing, leaving her under profound shadow. Soon it would crush her down completely.

Sparks?—or eyes looking at her across the water? She gazed, hypnotized. And with her sharp eyes she made out in the dusk the pale form of a bob-cat crouching by the water's edge, pale as the stones among which it crouched, opposite. And it was watching her with cold, electric eyes of strange intentness, a sort of cold, icy wonder and fearlessness. She saw its *museau* pushed forward, its tufted ears pricking intensely up. It was watching her with cold, animal curiosity, something demonish and conscienceless.

She made a swift movement, spilling her water. And in a flash the creature was gone, leaping like a cat that is escaping; but strange and soft in its motion, with its little bob-tail. Rather fascinating. Yet that cold, intent, demonish watching! She shivered with cold and fear. She knew well enough the dread and repulsiveness of the wild.

From *THE PLUMED SERPENT*

It was a long way, a long way through the peculiar squalid endings of the town, then along the straight road between trees, into the valley. The sun of April was brilliant, there were piles of cloud about the sky, where the volcanoes would be. The valley stretched away to its sombre, atmospheric hills, in a flat dry bed, parched except where there was some crop being irrigated. The soil seemed strange, dry, blackish, artificially wetted, and old. The trees rose high, and hung bare boughs, or withered shade. The buildings were either new and alien, like the Country Club, or cracked and dilapidated, with all the plaster falling off. The falling of thick plaster from cracked buildings—one could almost hear it.

Yellow tram-cars rushed at express speed away down the fenced-in car-lines, rushing round towards Xochimilco or Tlalpam. The asphalt road ran outside these lines, and on the asphalt rushed incredibly dilapidated Ford omnibuses, crowded with blank dark natives in dirty cotton clothes and big straw hats. At the far edge of the road, on the dust-tracks under the trees, little donkeys under huge loads loitered towards the city, driven by men with blackened faces and bare, blackened legs. Three-fold went the traffic; the roar of the tram-trains, the clatter of the automobiles, the straggle of asses and of outside-seeming individuals.

Occasional flowers would splash out in colour from a ruin of falling plaster. Occasional women with strong, dark-brown arms would be washing rags in a drain. An occasional horseman would ride across to the herd of motionless black-and-white cattle on the field. Occasional maize fields were already coming green. And the pillars that mark the water conduits passed one by one.

They went through the tree-filled plaza of Tlacolula, where natives were squatting on the ground, selling fruits or sweets, then down a road between high walls. They pulled up at last at big gate-doors, beyond which was a heavy pink-and-yellow house, and beyond the house, high, dark cypress trees.

In the road two motor-cars were already standing. That meant other visitors. Owen knocked on the studded fortress doors: there was an imbecile barking of dogs. At last a little footman with a little black moustache opened silently.

The square, inner patio, dark, with sun lying on the heavy arches of one side, had pots of red and white flowers, but was ponderous, as if dead for centuries. A certain dead, heavy strength and beauty seemed there, unable to pass away, unable to liberate itself and decompose. There was a stone basin of clear but motionless water, and the heavy reddish-and-yellow arches went round the courtyard with warrior-like fatality, their bases in dark shadow. Dead, massive house of the Conquistadores, with a glimpse of tall-grown garden beyond, and farther Aztec cypresses rising to strange dark heights. And dead silence, like the black, porous, absorptive lava rock. Save when the tram-cars battered past outside the solid wall.

* * *

She climbed up to the flat roofs of the hotel. It was a brilliant morning, and for once, under the blue sky of the distance, Popocatepetl stood aloof, a heavy giant presence under heaven, with a cape of snow. And rolling a long dark roll of smoke like a serpent.

Ixtaccihuatl, the White Woman, glittered and seemed near, but the other mountain, Popocatepetl, stood farther back, and in shadow, a pure cone of atmospheric shadow, with glinting flashes of snow. There they were, the two monsters, watching gigantically and terribly over their lofty, bloody cradle of men, the Valley of Mexico. Alien, ponderous, the white-hung mountains seemed to emit a deep purring sound too deep for the ear to hear, and yet audible on the blood, a sound of dead. There was no soaring or uplift or exaltation, as there is in the snowy mountains of Europe. Rather a ponderous white-shouldered weight, pressing terribly on the earth, and murmuring like two watchful lions.

Superficially, Mexico might be all right: with its suburbs of villas, its central fine streets, its thousands of motor-cars, its tennis and its bridge-parties. The sun shone brilliantly every day, and big bright flowers stood out from the trees. It was a holiday.

Until you were alone with it. And then the undertone was like the low angry, snarling purring of some jaguar spotted with night. There was a ponderous, down-pressing weight upon the spirit: the great folds of the dragon of the Aztecs, the dragon of the Toltecs, winding around one and weighing down the soul. And on the bright sunshine was a dark steam of an angry, impotent blood, and the flowers seemed to have their roots in spilt blood. The spirit of place was cruel, down-dragging, destructive.

Kate could so well understand the Mexican who had said to her: *El Grito mexicano es siempre el Grito del Odio*—The Mexicano shout is always a shout of hate. The famous revolutions, as Don Ramón said, began with *Viva!* but ended always with *Muera!* Death to this, death to the other, it was all death! death! death! as insistent as the Aztec sacrifices. Something for ever gruesome and macabre.

Why had she come to this high plateau of death? As a woman, she suffered even more than men suffer: and in the end, practically all men go under. Once, Mexico had had an elaborate ritual of death. Now it has death ragged, squalid, vulgar, without even the passion of its own mystery.

She sat on a parapet of the old roof. The street beyond was like a black abyss, but around her was the rough glare of uneven flat roofs, with loose telephone wires trailing across, and the sudden, deep, dark wells of the patios, showing flowers blooming in shade.

Just behind was a huge old church, its barrel roof humping up like some crouching animal, and its domes, like bubbles inflated, glittering with yellow tiles, and blue and white tiles, against the intense blue heaven. Quiet native women in long skirts were moving on the roofs, hanging out washing or spreading it on the stones. Chickens perched here and there. An occasional bird soared huge overhead, trailing a shadow. And not far away stood the brownish tower-stumps of the Cathedral, the profound old bell trembling huge and deep, so soft as to be almost inaudible, upon the air.

It ought to have been all gay, allegro, allegretto, in that sparkle of bright air and old roof surfaces. But no! There was the dark undertone, the black, serpent-like fatality all the time.

* * *

Mexico! The great, precipitous, dry, savage country, with a handsome church in every landscape, rising as it were out of nothing. A revolution-broken landscape, with lingering, tall handsome churches whose domes are like inflations that are going to burst, and whose pinnacles and towers are like the trembling pagodas of an unreal race. Gorgeous churches waiting, above the huts and straw hovels of the natives, like ghosts to be dismissed.

And noble, ruined haciendas, with ruined avenues approaching their broken splendour.

And the cities of Mexico, great and small, that the Spaniards conjured up out of nothing. Stones live and die with the spirit of the builders. And the spirit of Spaniards in Mexico dies, and the very stones in the building die. The natives drift into the centre of the plazas again, and in unspeakable empty weariness the Spanish buildings stand around, in a sort of dry exhaustion.

The conquered race! Cortés came with his iron heel and

his iron will, a conqueror. But a conquered race, unless grafted with a new inspiration, slowly sucks the blood of the conquerors, in the silence of a strange night and the heaviness of a hopeless will. So that now, the race of the conquerors in Mexico is soft and boneless, children crying in helpless hopelessness.

Was it the dark negation of the continent?

Kate could not look at the stones of the National Museum in Mexico without depression and dread. Snakes coiled like excrement, snakes fanged and feathered beyond all dreams of dread. And that was all.

The ponderous pyramids of San Juan Teotihuacan, the House of Quetzalcoatl wreathed with the snake of all snakes, his huge fangs white and pure to-day as in the lost centuries when his makers were alive. He has not died. He is not so dead as the Spanish churches, this all-enwreathing dragon of the horror of Mexico.

Cholula, with its church where the altar was! And the same ponderousness, the same unspeakable sense of weight and downward pressure of the blunt pyramid. Down-sinking pressure and depression. And the great market-place with its lingering dread and fascination.

Mitla under its hills, in the parched valley where a wind blows the dust and the dead souls of the vanished race in terrible gusts. The carved courts of Mitla, with a hard, sharp-angled, intricate fascination, but the fascination of fear and repellance. Hard, four-square, sharp-edged, cutting, zigzagging Mitla, like continual blows of a stone axe. Without gentleness or grace or charm. Oh America, with your unspeakable hard lack of charm, what then is your final meaning? Is it forever the knife of sacrifice, as you put out your tongue at the world?

Charmless America! With your hard, vindictive beauty, are you waiting forever to smite death? Is the world your everlasting victim?

* * *

The evening for once was grey: the rainy season really approaching. A sudden wind whirled dust and a few spots of rain. The train drew out of the formless, dry, dust-smitten areas fringing the city, and wound mildly on for a few minutes, only to stop in the main street of Tacubaya, the suburb-village. In the grey approach of evening the train halted heavily in the street, and Kate looked out at the men who stood in groups, with their hats tilted against the wind and their blankets folded over their shoulders and up to their eyes, against the dust, motionless, standing like sombre ghosts, only a glint of eyes showing between the dark sarape and the big hat-brim; while donkey-drivers in a dust-cloud ran frantically, with uplifted arms like demons, uttering short, sharp cries to prevent their donkeys from poking in between the coaches of the train. Silent dogs trotted in and out under the train, women, their faces wrapped in their blue rebozos came to offer tortillas folded in a cloth to keep them warm, or pulque in an earthenware mug, or pieces of chicken smothered in red, thick, oily sauce; or oranges or bananas or pitahayas, anything. And when few people bought, because of the dust, the women put their wares under their arm, under the blue rebozo, and covered their faces and motionless watched the train.

It was about six o'clock. The earth was utterly dry and stale. Somebody was kindling charcoal in front of a house. Men were hurrying down the wind, balancing their great hats curiously. Horsemen on quick, fine little horses, guns slung behind, trotted up to the train, lingered, then trotted quickly away again into nowhere.

Still the train stood in the street. Kate and Villiers got down. They watched the sparks blowing from the charcoal which a little girl was kindling in the street, to cook tortillas.

The train had a second-class coach and a first-class. The second-class was jam-full of peasants, Indians, piled in like chickens with their bundles and baskets and bottles, endless things. One woman had a fine peacock under her arm. She put it down and in vain tried to suppress it beneath her voluminous skirts. It refused to be suppressed. She took it up and balanced it on her knee, and looked round again over the medley of jars, baskets, pumpkins, melons, guns, bundles and human beings.

In the front was a steel car with a guard of little scrubby

soldiers in their dirty cotton uniforms. Some soldiers were mounted on top of the train with their guns: the look-out.

And the whole train, seething with life, was curiously still, subdued. Perhaps it is the perpetual sense of danger which makes the people so hushed, without clamour or stridency. And with an odd, hushed politeness among them. A sort of demon-world.

At last the train moved on. If it had waited for ever, no one would have been deeply surprised. For what might not be ahead? Rebels, bandits, bridges blown up—anything.

However, quietly, stealthily, the train moved out and along the great weary valley. The circling mountains, so relentless, were invisible save near at hand. In a few broken adobe huts, a bit of fire sparked red. The adobe was grey-black, of the lava dust, depressing. Into the distance the fields spread dry, with here and there patches of green irrigation. There was a broken hacienda with columns that supported nothing. Darkness was coming, dust still blew in the shadow; the valley seemed encompassed in a dry, stale, weary gloom.

Then there came a heavy shower. The train was passing a pulque hacienda. The rows of the giant maguey stretched bristling their iron-black barbs in the gloom.

* * *

She climbed with Villiers down the broken bank to the river, and in a moment they were in the boat. Pale green willow trees fringed from the earthen banks to the fuller-flowing, pale-brown water. The river was not very wide, between deep banks. They slipped under the bridge, and past a funny high barge with rows of seats. The boatman said it went up the river to Jocotlan: and he waved his hand to show the direction. They were slipping downstream, between lonely banks of willow-trees.

The crippled boatman was pulling hard, with great strength and energy. When she spoke to him in her bad Spanish and he found it hard to understand, he knitted his brow a little, anxiously. And when she laughed he smiled at her with such a beautiful gentleness, sensitive, wistful, quick. She felt he was naturally honest and truthful, and generous. There was a beauty in these men, a wistful beauty and a great physical strength. Why had she felt so bitterly about the country?

Morning was still young on the pale buff river, between the silent earthen banks. There was a blue dimness in the lower air, and black water-fowl ran swiftly, unconcernedly back and forth from the river's edge, on the dry, baked banks that were treeless now, and wider. They had entered a wide river, from the narrow one. The blueness and moistness of the dissolved night seemed to linger under the scattered pepper-trees of the far shore.

The boatman rowed short and hard upon the flimsy, soft, sperm-like water, only pausing at moments swiftly to smear the sweat from his face with an old rag he kept on the bench beside him. The sweat ran from his bronze-brown skin like water, and the black hair on his high-domed, Indian head smoked with wetness.

"There is no hurry," said Kate, smiling to him.

"What does the Señorita say?"

"There is no hurry," she repeated.

He paused, smiling, breathing deeply, and explained that now he was rowing against stream. This wider river flowed out of the lake, full and heavy. See! even as he rested a moment, the boat began to turn and drift! He quickly took his oars.

The boat moved slowly, in the hush of departed night, upon the soft, full-flowing buff water, that carried little tufts of floating water-hyacinth. Some willow-trees stood near the edge, and some pepper-trees of most delicate green foliage. Beyond the trees and the level of the shores, big hills rose up to high, blunt points, baked incredibly dry, like biscuit. The blue sky settled against them nakedly, they were leafless and lifeless save for the iron-green shafts of the organ cactus, that glistered blackly, yet atmospherically, in the ochreous aridity. This was Mexico again, stark-dry and luminous with powerful light, cruel and unreal.

On a flat near the river a peon, perched on the rump of his ass, was slowly driving five luxurious cows towards the water to drink. The big black-and-white animals stepped in a dream-pace past the pepper-trees to the bank, like moving pieces of light-and-shade: the dun cows trailed after, in the incredible silence and brilliance of the morning.

Earth, air, water were all silent with new light, the last blue of night dissolving like a breath. No sound, even no life. The great light was stronger than life itself. Only, up in the blue, some turkey-buzzards were wheeling with dirty-edged wings, as everywhere in Mexico.

* * *

There was a sound of breaking water. The boatman drew away, and pointed across to where a *canoa*, a native sailing-boat, was lying at an angle. She had run aground in a wind, and now must wait till another wind would carry her off the submerged bank again. Another boat was coming down the breeze, steering cautiously among the shoals, for the river outlet. She was piled high with petates, the native leaf-mats, above her hollowed black sides. And bare-legged men with loose white drawers rolled up, and brown chests showing, were running with poles as the shallows heaved up again, pushing her off, and balancing their huge hats with small, bird-like shakes of the head.

Beyond the boats, seawards, were rocks outcropping and strange birds like pelicans standing in silhouette, motionless.

They had been crossing a bay of the lake-shore, and were nearing the hotel. It stood on a parched dry bank above the pale-brown water, a long, low building amid a tender green of bananas and pepper-trees. Everywhere the shores rose up pale and cruelly dry, dry to cruelty, and on the little hills the dark statues of the organ cactus poised in nothingness.

There was a broken-down landing-place, and a boathouse in the distance, and someone in white flannel trousers was standing on the broken masonry. Upon the filmy water ducks and black water-fowl bobbed like corks. The bottom was stony. The boatman suddenly backed the boat, and pulled round. He pushed up his sleeve and hung over the bows, reaching into the water. With a quick motion he grabbed something, and scrambled into the boat again. He was holding in the pale-skinned hollow of his palm a little earthenware pot, crusted by the lake deposit.

"What is it?" she said.

"Ollitta of the gods," he said. "Of the old dead gods. Take it, Señorita."

* * *

She went up to her room, pausing at the corridor window to look out at the savage little hills that stood at the back of the hotel in desiccated heaps, with the dark-green bulks of organ-cactus sticking up mechanically and sinister, sombre in all the glare. Grey ground-squirrels like rats slithered ceaselessly around. Sinister, strangely dark and sinister, in the great glare of the sun!

She went to her room to be alone. Below her window, in the bricks and fallen rubble of unfinished masonry, a huge white turkey-cock, dim-white, strutted with his brown hens. And sometimes he stretched out his pink wattles and gave vent to fierce, powerful turkey-yelps, like some strong dog yelping; or else he ruffled all his feathers like a great, soiled white peony, and chuffed, hissing here and there, raging the metal of his plumage.

Below him, the eternal tremble of pale-earth, unreal waters, far beyond which rose the stiff resistance of mountains losing their pristine blue. Distinct, frail distances far off on the dry air, dim-seeing, yet sharp and edged with menace.

Kate took her bath in the filmy water that was hardly like water at all. Then she went and sat on the collapsed masonry, in the shade of the boat-house below. Small white ducks bobbed about on the shallow water below her, or dived, raising clouds of submarine dust. A canoe came paddling in; a lean fellow with sinewy brown legs. He answered Kate's nod with the aloof promptness of an Indian, made fast his canoe inside the boat-house, and was gone, stepping silent and barefoot over the bright green water-stones, and leaving a shadow, cold as flint, on the air behind him.

No sound on the morning save a faint touching of water, and the occasional powerful yelping of the turkey-cock. Silence, an aboriginal, empty silence, as of life *withheld.* The vacuity of a Mexican morning. Resounding sometimes to the turkey-cock.

And the great, lymphatic expanse of water, like a sea, trembling, trembling, trembling to a far distance, to the mountains of substantial nothingness.

Near at hand, a ragged shifting of banana trees, bare hills with immobile cactus, and to the left, a hacienda with peons' square mud boxes of houses. An occasional ranchero in skin-tight trousers and big hat, rode trotting through the dust on a small horse, or peons on the rump of their asses, in floppy white cotton, going like ghosts.

Always something ghostly. The morning passing all of a piece, empty, vacuous. All sound withheld, all life withheld, everything *holding back.* The land so dry as to have a quality of invisibility, the water earth-filmy, hardly water at all. The lymphatic milk of fishes, somebody said.

* * *

The sun rose, and a whiteness of light played on the tops of the mountains. The boat hugged the north shore, turning the promontory on which the villas had started so jauntily, twenty years ago, but now were lapsing back to wilderness. All was still and motionless in the light. Sometimes, on the little bare patches high up on the dry hills were white specks ; birds ? No, men in their white cotton, peons hoeing. They were so tiny and so distinct, they looked like white birds settled.

Round the bend were the hot springs, the church, the inaccessible village of the pure Indians, who spoke no Spanish. There were some green trees, under the precipitous, dry mountain-side.

So on and on, the motor-boat chugging incessantly, the man in the bows coiled up like a serpent, watching ; the fish-milk water gleaming and throwing off a dense light, so that the mountains away across were fused out. And Kate, under the awning, went into a kind of sleep.

They were passing the island, with its ruins of fortress and prison. It was all rock and dryness, with great broken walls and the shell of a church among its hurtful stones and its dry, grey herbage. For a long time the Indians had defended it against the Spaniards. Then the Spaniards used the island as a fortress against the Indians. Later, as a penal settlement. And now the place was a ruin, repellent, full of scorpions, and otherwise empty of life. Only one or two fishermen lived in the tiny cove facing the mainland, and a flock of goats, specks of life creeping among the rocks. And an unhappy fellow put there by the Government to register the weather.

* * *

A little steamer was smoking, lying off from a wooden jetty in the loneliness, and black, laden boats were poling out to her, and merging back to shore. The vessel gave a hoot, and slowly yet busily set off on the bosom of the water, heading in a slanting line across the lake, to where the tiny high white twin-towers of Tuliapán showed above the water-line, tiny and far-off, on the other side.

They had passed the jetty, and rounding the shoal where the willows grew, she could see Sayula; white fluted twin-towers of the church, obelisk shaped above the pepper-trees; beyond, a mound of a hill standing alone, dotted with dry bushes, distinct and Japanese looking; beyond this, the corrugated, blue-ribbed, flat-flanked mountains of Mexico.

It looked peaceful, delicate, almost Japanese. As she drew nearer she saw the beach with the washing spread on the sand; the fleecy green willow-trees and pepper-trees and the villas in foliage and flowers, hanging magenta curtains of bougainvillea, red dots of hibiscus, pink abundance of tall oleander trees; occasional palm-trees sticking out.

The boat was steering round a stone jetty, on which, in black letters, was painted an advertisement for motor-car tyres. There were a few seats, some deep fleecy trees growing out of the sand, a booth for selling drinks, a little promenade, and white boats on a sandy beach. A few women sitting under parasols, a few bathers in the water, and trees in front of the few villas deep in green or blazing scarlet blossoms.

* * *

The plaza now belonged to the peons. They sat thick on the benches, or slowly strolled round in their sandals and blankets. Across the cobbled road on the north side, the little booths selling soup and hot food were crowded with men, after six o'clock; it was cheaper to eat out, at the end of a day's work. The women at home could eat tortillas, never mind the *caldo*, the soup or the meat mess. At the booths which sold tequila, men, women, and boys sat on the benches with their elbows on the board. There was a mild gambling game, where the man in the centre turned the cards, and the plaza rang to his voice: *Cinco de Spadas! Rey de Copas!* A large, stout imperturbable woman, with a cigarette on her lip and danger in her lowering black eye, sat on into the night, selling tequila. The sweetmeat man stood by his board and sold sweets at one centavo each. And down on the pavement, small tin torch-lamps flared upon tiny heaps of mangoes or nauseous tropical red plums, two or three centavos the little heap, while the vendor, a woman in the full wave of her skirt, or a man with curious patient humility, squatted waiting for a purchaser, with that strange fatal indifference and that gentle sort of patience so puzzling to a stranger. To have thirty cents' worth of little red plums to sell; to pile them on the pavement in tiny pyramids, five in a pyramid; and to wait all day and on into the night, squatting on the pavement and looking up from the feet to the far-off face of the passer-by and potential purchaser, this, apparently, is an occupation and a living. At night by the flare of the tin torch, blowing its flame on the wind.

Usually there would be a couple of smallish young men with guitars of different sizes, standing close up facing one another like two fighting cocks that are uttering a long, endless swan-song, singing in tense subdued voices the eternal ballads, not very musical, mournful, endless, intense, audible only within close range; keeping on and on till their throats were scraped. And a few tall, dark men in red blankets standing around, listening casually, and rarely, very rarely making a contribution of one centavo.

In among the food booths would be another trio, this time two guitars and a fiddle, and two of the musicians blind; the blind ones singing at a high pitch, full speed, yet not very audible. The very singing seemed secretive, the singers pressing close in, face to face, as if to keep the wild, melancholy ballad re-echoing in their private breasts, their backs to the world.

And the whole village was in the plaza, it was like a camp, with the low, rapid sound of voices. Rarely, very rarely a voice rose above the deep murmur of the men, the musical ripple of the women, the twitter of the children. Rarely any quick movement; the slow promenade of men in sandals, the sandals, called huaraches, making a slight cockroach shuffle on the pavement. Sometimes, darting among the trees, bare-legged boys went sky-larking in and out of the shadow, in and out of the quiet people. They were the irrepressible boot-blacks, who swarm like tiresome flies in a bare-footed country.

* * *

Morning! Brilliant sun pouring into the patio, on the hibiscus flowers and the fluttering yellow and green rags of the banana trees. Birds swiftly coming and going, with tropical suddenness. In the dense shadow of the mango-grove, white-clad Indians going like ghosts. The sense of fierce sun and almost more impressive, of dark, intense shadow. A twitter of life, yet a certain heavy weight of silence. A dazzling flicker and brilliance of light, yet the feeling of weight.

Kate would sit alone, rocking on her verandah, pretending to sew. Silently appears an old man with one egg held up mysteriously, like some symbol. Would the patrona buy it for five centavos? La Juana only gives four centavos. All right? Where is Juana?

Juana appears from the plaza with more purchases. The egg! The four centavos! The account of the spendings. *Entonces! Entonces! Luego! Luego! Ah, Niña, no tengo memoria!* Juana could not read nor write. She scuffled off to the market with her pesos, bought endless little things at one or two centavos each, every morning. And every morning there was a reckoning up. Ah! Ah! Where are we? I have no memory. Well then—ah—yes—I bought ocote for three centavos! How much? How much, Niña? How much is it now?

It was a game which thrilled Juana to the marrow, reckoning up the centavos to get it just right. If she was a centavo short in the change, she was paralysed. Time after time she would reappear. *There is a centavo short, Niña? Ah, how stupid I am! But I will give you one of mine!*

"Don't bother," said Kate. "Don't think of it any more."

"But yes. But yes!" and away she limped in distraction.

Till an hour later, loud cry from the far end of the house. Juana waving a scrap of greenery.

"Mire! Niña! Compré perjil a un centavo—I bought parsley for one cent. Is it right?"

"It is right," said Kate.

* * *

The morning was clear and hot, the pale brown lake quite still, like a phantom. People were moving on the beach, in the distance tiny, like dots of white: white dots of men following the faint dust of donkeys. She wondered often why humanity was like specks in the Mexican landscape; just specks of life.

They passed from the lake shore to the rough, dusty road going west, between the steep slope of the hills and the bit of flat by the lake. For almost a mile there were villas, most of them shut up fast, some of them smashed, with broken walls and smashed windows. Only flowers bloomed in masses above the rubble.

In the empty places were flimsy straw huts of the natives, haphazard, as if blown there. By the road under the hill, were black-grey adobe huts, like boxes, and fowls running about, and brown pigs or grey pigs spotted with black careered and grunted, and half-naked children, dark orange-brown, trotted or lay flat on their faces in the road, their little naked posteriors hutched up, fast asleep. Already asleep again.

The houses were many of them being re-thatched, or the tiled roofs were being patched by men who assumed a great air of importance at having undertaken such a task. They were pretending to hurry, too, because the real rains might begin any day. And in the little stony levels by the lake, the land was being scratch-ploughed by a pair of oxen and a lump of pointed wood.

But this part of the road Kate knew. She knew the fine villa on the knoll, with its tufts of palms, and the laid-out avenues that were laid out, indeed, as the dead are, to crumble back again. She was glad to be past the villas, where the road came down to the lake again, under big shady trees that had twisted, wriggly beans. On the left was the water, the colour of turtle doves, lapping the pale fawn stones. At a water-hole of a stream in the beach, a cluster of women were busily washing clothes. In the shallows of the lake itself two women sat bathing, their black hair hanging dense and wet. A little farther along, a man was wading slowly, stopping to throw his round net skilfully upon the water, then slowly stooping and gathering it in, picking out the tiny, glittery fish called charales. Strangely silent and remote everything, in the gleaming morning, as if it were some distant period of time.

A little breeze was coming from the lake, but the deep dust underfoot was hot. On the right the hill rose precipitous, baked and yellowish, giving back the sun and the intense dryness, and exhaling the faint, desiccated, peculiar smell of Mexico, that smells as if the earth had sweated itself dry.

All the time strings of donkeys trotted laden through the dust, their drivers stalking erect and rapid behind, watching with eyes like black holes, but always answering Kate's salute with a respectful *Adios!* And Juana echoed her laconic *Adiosn!* She was limping, and she thought it horrible of Kate to walk four miles, when they might have struggled out in an old hired motor-car, or gone in a boat, or even ridden donkey-back.

But to go on foot! Kate could hear all her criada's feelings in the drawled, sardonic *Adiosn!* But the man behind strode bravely and called cheerfully. His pistol was prominent in his belt.

A bluff of yellow rock came jutting at the road. The road wound round it, and into a piece of flat open country. There were fields of dry stone, and hedges of dusty thorn and cactus. To the left the bright green of the willows by the lake-shore. To the right the hills swerved inland, to meet the sheer, fluted sides of dry mountains. Away ahead, the hills curved back at the shore, and a queer little crack or niche showed. This crack in the hills led from Don Ramón's shore-property to the little valley where he grew the sugar cane. And where the hills approached the lake again, there was a dark clustering of mango trees, and the red upper-storey of the hacienda house.

"There it is!" cried the man behind. "Jamiltepec, Señorita. La hacienda de Don Ramón!"

✲ ✲ ✲

The evening breeze was blowing very faintly. Sailing-boats were advancing through the pearly atmosphere, far off, the sun above had a golden quality. The opposite shore, twenty miles away, was distinct, and yet there seemed an opalescent, spume-like haze in the air, the same quality as in the filmy water. Kate could see the white specks of the far-off church towers of Tuliapan.

Below, in the garden below the house, was a thick grove of mango-trees. Among the dark and reddish leaves of the mangos, scarlet little birds were bustling, like suddenly opening poppy-buds, and pairs of yellow birds, yellow underneath as yellow butterflies, so perfectly clear, went skimming past. When they settled for a moment and closed their wings, they disappeared, for they were grey on top. And when the cardinal birds settled, they too disappeared, for the outside of their wings was brown, like a sheath.

"Birds in this country have all their colour below," said Kate.

✲ ✲ ✲

The black wind was all loose in the sky, tearing with the thin shriek of torn fabrics, in the mango-trees. Men held their big hats on their heads and ran with bent knees, their serapes blowing. Women clutched their rebozos tighter and ran bare-foot to the zaguan.

The big doors were open, a soldier stood with a gun across his back, holding a hurricane lamp. And the people fled like ghosts through the doors, and away up the black lane like bits of paper veering away into nothingness, blown out of their line of flight. In a moment, they had all silently gone.

Martin barred the great doors. The soldier put down his lamp on the wooden bench, and he and his comrades sat huddled in their dark shawls, in a little bunch like toadstools in the dark cavern of the zaguan. Already one had curled himself up on the wooden bench, wrapped like a snail in his blanket, head disappeared.

"The water is coming!" cried the servants excitedly, as Kate went upstairs with Doña Carlota.

The lake was quite black, like a great pit. The wind suddenly blew with violence, with a strange ripping sound in the mango-trees, as if some membrane in the air were being ripped. The white-flowered oleanders in the garden below leaned over quite flat, their white flowers ghostly, going right down to the earth, in the pale beam of the lamp—like a street lamp—that shone on the wall at the front entrance. A young palm-tree bent and spread its leaves on the ground. Some invisible juggernaut car rolling in the dark over the outside world.

Away across the lake, south-west, lightning blazed and ran down the sky like some portentous writing. And soft velvety thunder broke inwardly, strangely.

"It frightens me!" cried Doña Carlota, putting her hand over her eyes and hastening into a far corner of the bare salon.

Cipriano and Kate stood on the terrace, watching the coloured flowers in the pots shake and fly to bits, disappearing up into the void of darkness. Kate clutched her shawl. But the wind suddenly got under Cipriano's blanket, and lifted it straight up in the air, then dropped it in a scarlet flare over his head. Kate watched his deep, strong Indian chest lift as his arms quickly fought to free his head. How dark he was, and how primitively physical, beautiful and deep-breasted, with soft, full flesh! But all, as it were, for himself. Nothing that came forth from him to meet with one outside. All oblivious of the outside, all for himself.

"Ah! the water!" he cried, holding down his serape.

The first great drops were flying darkly at the flowers, like arrows. Kate stood back into the doorway of the salon. A pure blaze of lightning slipped three-fold above the black hills, seemed to stand a moment, then slip back into the dark.

Down came the rain with a smash, as if some great vessel had broken. With it came a waft of icy air. And all the time, first in one part of the sky, then in another, in quick succession the blue lightning, very blue, broke out of heaven and lit up the air for a blue, breathless moment, looming trees and ghost of a garden, then was gone, while thunder dropped and exploded continually.

Kate watched the dropping masses of water in wonder. Already, in the blue moments of lightning, she saw the garden below a pond, the walks were rushing rivers. It was cold. She turned indoors.

A servant was going round the rooms with a lantern, to look if scorpions were coming out. He found one scuttling across the floor of Kate's room, and one fallen from the ceiling beams on to Carlota's bed.

* * *

Kate nearly always went out about five o'clock, on Saturdays, to see the boats, flat-bottomed, drift up to the shallow shores, and begin to unload in the glow of the evening. It pleased her to see the men running along the planks with the dark-green melons, and piling them in a mound on the rough sand, melons dark-green like creatures with pale bellies. To see the tomatoes all poured out into a shallow place in the lake, bobbing about while the women washed them, a bobbing scarlet upon the water.

The long, heavy bricks were piled in heaps along the scrap of demolished break-water, and little gangs of asses came trotting down the rough beach, to be laden, pressing their little feet in the gravelly sand, and flopping their ears.

The cargadores were busy at the charcoal boats, carrying out the rough sacks.

"Do you want charcoal, Niña?" shouted a grimy cargador, who had carried the trunks from the station on his back.

"At how much?"

"Twenty-five reales the two sacks."

"I pay twenty reales."

"At twenty reales then, Señorita. But you give me two reales for the transport?"

"The owner pays the transport," said Kate. "But I will give you twenty centavos."

Away went the man, trotting barelegged, barefoot, over the stony ground, with two large sacks of charcoal on his shoulders. The men carry huge weights, without seeming ever to think they are heavy. Almost as if they liked to feel a huge weight crushing on their iron spines, and to be able to resist it.

Baskets of spring guavas, baskets of sweet lemons called limas, baskets of tiny green and yellow lemons, big as walnuts; orange-red and greenish mangoes, oranges, carrots, cactus fruits in great abundance, a few knobby potatoes, flat, pearl-white onions, little calabasitas and speckled green calabasitas like frogs, camotes cooked and raw—she loved to watch the baskets trotting up the beach past the church.

Then, rather late as a rule, big red pots, bulging red ollas for water-jars, earthenware casseroles and earthenware jugs with cream and black scratched pattern in glaze, bowls, big flat earthenware discs for cooking tortillas—much earthenware.

On the west shore, men were running up the beach wearing twelve enormous hats at once, like a trotting pagoda. Men trotting with finely woven huaraches and rough strip sandals. And men with a few dark serapes, with gaudy rose-pink patterns, in a pile on their shoulders.

It was fascinating. But at the same time, there was a heavy, almost sullen feeling on the air. These people came to market to a sort of battle. They came, not for the joy of selling, but for the sullen contest with those who wanted what they had got. The strange, black resentment always present.

By the time the church bells clanged for sunset, the market had already begun. On all the pavements round the plaza squatted the Indians with their wares, pyramids of green watermelons, arrays of rough earthenware, hats in piles, pairs of sandals side by side, a great array of fruit, a spread of collar-studs and knick-knacks, called *novedades*, little trays with sweets.

And people arriving all the time out of the wild country, with laden asses.

Yet never a shout, hardly a voice to be heard. None of the animation and the frank wild clamour of a Mediterranean market. Always the heavy friction of the will; always, always, grinding upon the spirit, like the grey-black grind of lava-rock.

* * *

She drank her coffee on the verandah, and the heavy papayas in their grouping seemed to be oozing like great drops from the invisible spouting of the fountain of non-human life. She seemed to see the great sprouting and urging of the cosmos, moving into weird life. And men only like green-fly clustering on the tender tips, an aberration there. So monstrous the rolling and unfolding of the life of the cosmos, as if even iron could grow like lichen deep in the earth, and cease growing, and prepare to perish. Iron and stone render up their life, when the hour comes. And men are less than the green-fly sucking the stems of the bush, so long as they live by business and bread alone. Parasites on the face of the earth.

She strayed to the shore. The lake was blue in the morning light, the opposite mountains pale and dry and ribbed like mountains in the desert. Only at their feet, next the lake, the dark strip of trees and white specks of villages.

Near her, against the light, five cows stood with their noses to the water, drinking. Women were kneeling on the stones, filling red jars. On forked sticks stuck up on the foreshore, frail fishing nets were hung out, drying, and on the nets a small bird sat facing the sun; he was red as a drop of new blood, from the arteries of the air.

* * *

Along the edge of the water flew four dark birds, their necks pushed out, skimming silent near the silent surface of the lake, in a jagged level rush.

Kate knew these mornings by the lake. They hypnotized her almost like death. Scarlet birds like drops of blood, in very green willow-trees. The aquador trotting to her house with a pole over his shoulder, and two heavy square gasoline cans, one at each end of the pole, filled with hot water. He had been to the hot spring for her daily supply. Now barefoot, with one bare leg, the young man trotted softly beneath the load, his dark, handsome face sunk beneath the shadows of the big hat, as he trotted in a silence, mindlessness that was like death.

Dark heads out on the water in little groups, like black water-fowl bobbing. Were they birds ? Were they heads ? Was this human life, or something intermediate, that lifted its orange, wet, glistening shoulders a little out of the lake, beneath the dark head ?

She knew so well what the day would be. Slowly the sun thickening and intensifying in the air overhead. And slowly the electricity clotting invisibly as afternoon approached. The beach in the blind heat, strewn with refuse, smelling of refuse and the urine of creatures.

Everything going vague in the immense sunshine, as the air invisibly thickened, and Kate could feel the electricity pressing like hot iron on the back of her head. It stupefied her like morphine. Meanwhile the clouds rose like white trees from behind the mountains, as the afternoon swooned in silence, rose and spread black branches, quickly, in the sky, from which the lightning stabbed like birds.

And in the midst of the siesta stupor, the sudden round bolts of thunder, and the crash and the chill of the rain.

Tea-time, and evening coming. The last sailing-boats making to depart, waiting for the wind. The wind was from the west, the boats going east and south had gone, their sails were lapsing far away on the lake. But the boats towards the west were waiting, waiting, while the water rattled under their black, flat keels.

* * *

The church inside was a dead interior, like all Mexican churches, even the gorgeous Puebla cathedral. The interior of almost any Mexican church gives the impression of cynical barrenness, cynical meaninglessness, an empty, cynical, mocking shell. The Italian churches are built much in the same style, and yet in them lingers a shadow and stillness of old, mysterious holiness. The hush.

But not in Mexico. The churches outside are impressive. Inside, and it is curious to define it, they are blatant ; void of sound and yet with no hush, simple, and yet completely vulgar, barren, sterile. More barren than a bank or a schoolroom or an empty concert-hall, less mysterious than any of these. You get a sense of plaster, of mortar, of whitewash, of smeared blue-wash or grey-wash ; and of gilt laid on and ready to peel off. Even in the most gorgeous churches, the gilt is hatefully gilt, never golden. Nothing is soft nor mellow.

So the interior of Sayula church ; and Kate had often been in. The white exterior was charming, and so valuable in the landscape, with the twin white pagoda-towers peering out of the green willow-trees. But inside, it seemed nothing but whitewash, stencilled over with grey scroll-work decorations. The windows were high, and many, letting in the light as into a schoolroom. Jesus, streaked with blood was in one of the transepts, and the Virgin, a doll in faded satin, stood startled inside a glass case. There were rag flowers and paper flowers, coarse lace and silver that looked like tin.

* * *

In the zaguan was a great heap of silky white wool, very fine, and in the dark corridor of the patio all the people at work. Two boys with flat square boards bristling with many little wire bristles were carding the white wool into thin films, which they took off the boards in fine rolls like mist, and laid beside the two girls at the end of the shed.

These girls stood by their wheels, spinning, standing beside the running wheel, which they set going with one hand, while with the other hand they kept a long, miraculous thread of white wool-yarn dancing at the very tip of the rapidly-spinning spool-needle, the filmy rolls of the carded wool just touching the point of the spool, and at once running out into a long, pure thread of white, which wound itself on to the spool, and another piece of carded wool was attached. One of the girls, a beautiful oval-faced one, who smiled shyly at Kate, was very clever. It was almost miraculous the way she touched the spool and drew out the thread of wool almost as fine as sewing cotton.

At the other end of the corridor, under the black shed, were two looms, and two men weaving. They treadled at the wooden tread-looms, first with one foot and then the other, absorbed and silent, in the shadow of the black mud walls. One man was weaving a brilliant scarlet serape, very fine, and of the beautiful cochineal red. It was difficult work. From the pure scarlet centre zigzags of black and white were running in a sort of whorl, away to the edge, that was pure black. Wonderful to see the man, with small bobbins of fine red and white yarn, and black, weaving a bit of the ground, weaving the zigzag of black up to it, and, up to that, the zigzag of white, with deft, dark fingers, quickly adjusting his setting needle, quick as lightning threading his pattern, then bringing down the beam heavily to press it tight. The serape was woven on a black warp, long fine threads of black, like a harp. But beautiful beyond words the perfect, delicate scarlet weaving in.

* * *

She opened her bedroom window one morning, and looked down to the lake. The sun had come, and queer blotty shadows were on the hills beyond the water. Way down at the water's edge a woman was pouring water from a calabash bowl over a statuesque pig, dipping rapidly and assiduously. The little group was seen in silhouette against the pale, dun lake.

But impossible to stand at her open window looking on the little lane. An old man suddenly appeared from nowhere, offering her a leaf full of tiny fish, charales, like splinters of glass, for ten centavos, and a girl was unfolding three eggs from the ragged corner of her rebozo, thrusting them imploringly forward to Kate. An old woman was shambling up with a sad story, Kate knew. She fled from her window and the importunity.

At the same instant, the sound that always made her heart stand still woke on the invisible air. It was the sound of drums, of tom-toms rapidly beaten. The same sound she had heard in the distance, in the tropical dusk of Ceylon, from the temple at sunset. The sound she had heard from the edge of the forests in the north, when the Red Indians were dancing by the fire. The sound that wakes dark, ancient echoes in the heart of every man, the thud of the primeval world.

Two drums were violently throbbing against each other. Then gradually they were slowing down, in a peculiar uneven rhythm, till at last there was only left one slow, continual monotonous note, like a great drop of darkness falling heavily, continually, dripping in the bright morning.

* * *

The rainy season had almost passed, though throughout September and even in October occasional heavy downpours fell. But the wonderful Mexican autumn, like a strange, inverted spring, was upon the land. The waste places bloomed with pink and white cosmos, the strange wild trees flowered in a ghostly way, forests of small sunflowers shone in the sun, the sky was a pure, pure blue, the floods of sunshine lay tempered on the land, that in part was flooded with water, from the heavy rains.

The lake was very full, strange and uneasy, and it had washed up a bank of the wicked water-hyacinths along all its shores. The wild-fowl were coming from the north, clouds of wild ducks like dust in the high air, sprinkling the water like weeds. Many, many wild-fowl, grebe, cranes, and white gulls of the inland seas, so that the northern mystery seemed to have blown so far south. There was a smell of water in the land, and a sense of soothing. For Kate firmly believed that part of the horror of the Mexican people came from the unsoothed dryness of the land and the untempered crudity of the flat-edged sunshine. If only there could be a softening of water in the air, and a haze above trees, the unspoken and unspeakable malevolence would die out of the human hearts.

Kate rode out often with Teresa to see the fields. The sugar-cane in the inner valley was vivid green, and rising tall, tall. The peons were beginning to cut it with their sword-like machetes, filling the bullock-wagons, to haul the cane to the factory in Sayula. On the dry hill-slopes the spikey tequila plant—a sort of maguey—flourished in its iron wickedness.

Low wild cactuses put forth rose-like blossoms, wonderful and beautiful for such sinister plants. The beans were gathered from the bean-fields, some gourds and squashes still sprawled their uncanny weight across the land. Red chillies hung on withering plants, red tomatoes sank to the earth. Some maize still reared its flags, there was still young corn to eat on the cob. The banana crop was small, the children came in with the little wild yellow tejocote apples, for making preserves. Teresa was making preserves, even with the late figs and peaches. On the trees, the ponderous mango-trees, some fruit was again orange-yellow and ripe, but the most still hung in strings, heavy and greenish and dropping like the testes of bulls.

It was autumn in Mexico, with wild duck on the waters, and hunters with guns, and small wild doves in the trees. Autumn in Mexico, and the coming of the dry season, with the sky higher and higher, pure pale blue, the sunset arriving with a strange flare of crystal yellow light. With the coffee berries turning red on the struggling bushes under the trees, and bougainvillea in the strong light glowing with a glow of magenta colour so deep you could plunge your arms deep in it. With a few humming-birds in the sunshine, and the fish in the waters gone wild, and the flies, that steamed black in the first rains, now passing away again.

* * *

She would sit alone for hours on the shore, under a green willow tree that hung its curtains of pale-green fronds on the beach. The lake was much fuller and higher up the shore, softer, more mysterious. There was a smell of the piles of water-hyacinth decaying at the water's edges. Distance seemed farther away. The near conical hills were dotted with green bushes, like a Japanese drawing. Bullock-wagons with solid wheels came rolling to the village, high with sugar-cane, drawn by eight oxen with ponderous heads and slowly swinging horns, while a peon walked in front with the guiding-stick on the cross-beam of the yoke. So slow, so massive, yet with such slight control.

She had a strange feeling, in Mexico, of the old pre-historic humanity, the dark-eyed humanity of the days, perhaps, before the glacial period. When the world was colder, and the seas emptier, and all the land-formation was different. When the waters of the world were piled in stupendous glaciers on the high places, and high, high upon the poles. When great plains stretched away to the oceans, like Atlantis and the lost continents of Polynesia, so that seas were only great lakes, and the soft, dark-eyed people of that world could walk around the globe. Then there was a mysterious, hot-blooded, soft-footed humanity with a strange civilization of its own.

Till the glaciers melted, and drove the peoples to the high places, like the lofty plateaux of Mexico, separated them into cut-off nations.

Sometimes, in America, the shadow of that old pre-Flood world was so strong, that the day of historic humanity would melt out of Kate's consciousness . . .

* * *

Suddenly before her she saw a long, dark soft rope, lying over a pale boulder. But her soul was softly alert, at once. It was a snake, with a subtle pattern along its soft dark back, lying there over a big stone, with its head sunk down to earth.

It felt her presence, too, for suddenly, with incredible soft quickness, it contracted itself down the boulder, and she saw it entering a little gap in the bottom of the wall.

The hole was not very big. And as it entered it quickly looked back, poising its little, dark, wicked, pointed head, and flickering a dark tongue. Then it passed on, slowly easing its dark length into the hole.

When it had all gone, Kate could see the last fold still, and the flat little head resting on the fold, like the devil with his chin on his arms, looking out of a loop-hole. So the wicked sparks of the eyes looked out at her, from within the recess. Watching out of its own invisibility.

So she wondered over it, as it lay in its hidden places. At all the unseen things in the hidden places of the earth. And she wondered if it was disappointed at not being able to rise higher in creation: to be able to run on four feet, and not keep its belly on the ground.

* * *

There was a certain autumnal purity and lull on the lake. The moisture still lingered, the bushes on the wild hills were green in puffs. Sunlight lay in a rich gleam on the mountains, and shadows were deep and velvety. The green almost covered the rocks and the pinkish land. Bright green the sugar-cane, red the ploughed earth, dark the trees with white specks of villages here and there. And over the wild places, a sprinkle of bushes, then stark grey rock still coming out.

The sky was very high and pure. In the morning came the sound of drums, and on the motionless, crystal air the cry for the pauses of the day. And always the day seemed to be pausing and unfolding again to the greater mystery. The universe seemed to have opened vast and soft and delicate with life.

There was something curiously soothing even in the full, pale, dove-brown water of the lake. A boat was coming over, with its sail hollowed out like a shell, pearly white, and its sharp black canoe-beak slipping past the water. It looked like the boat of Dionysos coming with a message, and the vine sprouting.

From *APOCALYPSE*

What man most passionately wants is his living wholeness and his living unison, not his own isolate salvation of his "soul." Man wants his physical fulfilment first and foremost, since now, once and once only, he is in the flesh and potent. For man, the vast marvel is to be alive. For man, as for flower and beast and bird, the supreme triumph is to be most vividly, most perfectly alive. Whatever the unborn and the dead may know, they cannot know the beauty, the marvel of being alive in the flesh. The dead may look after the afterwards. But the magnificent here and now of life in the flesh is ours, and ours alone, and ours only for a time. We ought to dance with rapture that we should be alive and in the flesh, and part of the living, incarnate cosmos. I am part of the sun as my eye is part of me. That I am part of the earth my feet know perfectly, and my blood is part of the sea. My soul knows that I am part of the human race, my soul is an organic part of the great human soul, as my spirit is part of my nation. In my own very self, I am part of my family. There is nothing of me that is alone and absolute except my mind, and we shall find that the mind has no existence by itself, it is only the glitter of the sun on the surface of the waters.

INDEX OF FIRST LINES

From *The White Peacock*

From *The Trespasser*

From *Sons and Lovers*

From *Sons and Lovers*—cont.

From *The Prussian Officer*

From *The Rainbow*

From *The Rainbow*—cont.

From *Women In Love*

From *Lady Chatterley's Lover*

From *The Lost Girl*

From *Aaron's Rod*

From *Aaron's Rod*—cont.

From *Kangaroo*—cont.

From *St. Mawr*

From *The Plumed Serpent*

From *The Plumed Serpent*—cont.

From *Apocalypse*